THE DIET FOOD FINDER

THE DIET FOOD FINDER

Joan T. Casale

R. R. Bowker Company
A Xerox Education Company
New York & London, 1975

Published by R. R. Bowker Co. (A Xerox Education Company)
1180 Avenue of the Americas, New York, N.Y. 10036
Copyright © 1975 by Joan T. Casale
Printed and bound in the United States of America

Library of Congress Cataloging in Publication Data

Casale, Joan T.
  The diet food finder.

  Bibliography: p.
  Includes indexes.
  1. Diet in disease—Abstracts.   I. Title
RM219.C38   613.2   75-15533
ISBN 0-8352-0783-8

To Nellie Barr Cagni

Contents

Preface

The field of diet cookery is a confusing mishmash of reliable information, freakish panaceas, well-meaning but inept interpretations of therapeutic diets, and production-line rehashes of assorted recipes to which a meaningless "diet" label has been attached. It is the purpose of this book to bring together recommended sources of reliable information considered as nutritionally sound and appropriate for the lay person. These sources, complied through a survey of the field, produced a bibliography of more than 200 recommended books and pamphlets providing information on 25 therapeutic and special diets as well as four topics under the general heading of Food and Nutrition Education. The sources include not only cookbooks, but supplementary books, brochures and product-related materials, foreign language materials, and periodicals. The recommended titles, arranged in order of preference, comprise the annotated bibliography of *The Diet Food Finder*.

The selection of therapeutic and special diet cookbooks was too important a task to be done by guesswork or by book jacket endorsements. Although the more outrageous examples of fad diets can be recognized by most persons possessing common sense and respect for the scientific method, it was necessary to consult experts. The experts had to possess both a scientific understanding of nutrition and practical experience in the everyday problems of the kitchen.

Scientists working in nutritional research are well aware of the latest discoveries in nutrition, but have little or no expertise in cookery. "Nutritionist" is such an ill-defined term that it can be assumed by anyone from a quack to a Ph.D. in biochemistry. Home economists may or may not specialize in foods, and usually do not have a strong college curriculum in the sciences.

It was decided that those most qualified to recommend diet cookbooks to the general public are registered dietitians. The reasons are simple. The term "registered dietitian," designated by the initials R.D., means the same thing in New York as it does in Alabama, Illinois, or California. Dietitians have a bachelor's degree in science and complete a dietetic internship or advanced degree before they can become registered with the American Dietetic Association. Registration, which follows the same standard throughout the United States, is maintained for five-year periods by completing 75 hours of continuing education. (This requirement was introduced in 1969 to insure high standards in the face of an ever-increasing body of knowledge.) In addition to their rigorous training and professional standards, most dietitians spend their careers advising patients on diet cookery, and they themselves usually are avid cooks. Finally, empirical observation of their book endorsements and reviews clearly demonstrates that they cannot be bought, enticed, or flattered into recommending a book that they think is inappropriate.

Queries about recommended diet cookbooks, therefore, were sent to registered dietitians across the country. This direct survey consisted of a one-page form sent to the heads of 50 state dietetic associations and to public health nutritionists in all 50 states and in the 20 largest cities. A rather complex survey form also was submitted to members of the San Diego District, California Dietetic Association. Recommendations were requested for cookbooks and supplementary books in selected diet categories. In all, nearly 50 persons responded with recommendations. In the case of public health departments, some 20 respondents did not identify themselves as registered dietitians, so their recommendations could not be used to determine book selection. Nonetheless, a number of books suggested by this group were obtained and submitted for review to either Patricia McNeece Kelly, R.D., or to Ruth Shear Reznikoff, R.D., of the San Diego District, California Dietetic Association. Book reviews were also consulted in the two leading journals that are published by dietitians, the *Journal of the American Dietetic Association*, and the *Journal of Nutrition Education*. Annotated bibliographies published by various dietetic associations, nutrition councils, and health departments likewise were culled for recommendations.

Although book selection was based on a consensus of registered dietitians whose professional standing is determined by the American Dietetic Association and book reviews published by dietitians, it must be stressed that this book is an independent work of the author, and is neither an official nor an unofficial project of any professional association or journal.

Some dietitians have recommended books that have not been included. Usually this is because the book has gone out of print, or the title was available only to state or county residents, and could not be suggested to a nationwide audience. With only one or two exceptions, books that received a single, overall negative review were dropped from consideration. A handful of books that are included contain statements that have been challenged by some reviewers. The cautionary notes of these reviewers are quoted or summarized in the annotations, and the sources are cited.

A number of recently published titles inevitably have been missed. The cut-off date for books included in this volume was August 1, 1974. Other books may not have come to the attention of the author, despite a thorough and far-reaching search. Noninclusion in *The Diet Food Finder*, therefore, should not necessarily be taken to mean that the book has been found unworthy—although that was the fate of many.

Despite the fact that the special character and range of recipes in each diet cookbook are described in the annotated bibliography, the cook, librarian, or dietitian may waste a great deal of time, or even money, searching for a particular recipe or type of recipes. To solve this problem, master recipe indexes were compiled for 10 diet categories, and for 11 subcategories under allergy diets. In all, approximately 15,000 recipes from 86 recommended cookbooks have been indexed in this book.

Because some diets call for special products which may not be found in every supermarket, Appendix 2 contains a list of retail mail-order suppliers, and Appendix 3 is a chart showing the special dietary foods that they offer.

More good cookbooks need to be written in a number of diet categories, and many of the present books can be improved. Indexes, for example, must be carefully prepared. Utilized to a great extent in preparing indexes for *The Diet Food Finder*, and recommended as a guide for any cookbook author or editor, is *Joy of Cooking* by Irma S. Rombauer and Marion R. Becker (Bobbs-Merrill, 1964); its excellent index spans basic American cookery and the most popular foreign favorites.

Incomplete ingredient control is another common weakness. Just as dietitians and qualified nutritionists constantly urge better ingredient identification in packaged and prepared foods, so too they must see that recipes in diet cookbooks bear more complete ingredient analyses. Countless recipes are appropriate for diets other than the single one with which they are identified, yet the average cook may have neither the capacity nor the desire to make a nutritional analysis. Unless ingredient control is completely spelled out, the potential for the multiple use of recipes is lost. Helpful examples of cookbooks offering good ingredient control information are Schoenberg's *Good Housekeeping Cookbook for Calorie Watchers* (entry 169) and Black and Carey's *Vegetarian Cookery* series (entries 200–204) which contains a complete computer analysis of each recipe for 17 nutritional factors.

These suggestions are the observations of a nonprofessional. Much more helpful for authors and editors—and ultimately, the dieter—would be a simple set of professionally created guidelines for writing diet cookbooks. Perhaps dietitians will assert their competence in this regard. The profession's "ladylike" modesty is an anachronism today, and does an injustice to the cause of good nutrition.

While commenting on the content and style of the diet cookbooks reviewed, it is impossible to remain silent about another common flaw. Too many books repeat old fashioned sexist clichés that demean not only adult men and women, but the importance of good nutrition: Food preparation is shown as exclusively women's work... Deprivation of red meat is presented as a threat to "masculinity"... Wives are "mothers" supervising the fat-controlled diets of their 60-year-old "boy" husbands... Weight reduction diets are equated with feminine vanity calculated to catch or hold a man... Only men become really sick while most women's illnesses are imaginary.

Such inaccurate stereotypes and absurd role-playing should have no place in works purporting to deal with an applied science. When otherwise good books are marred by this sort of nonsense, men are virtually forced to shun personal responsibility for controlling diets that seriously affect their health, and women are typecast in a series of unflattering, one-dimensional roles.

Nonetheless, something positive and heartening came through the review of diet cookbooks. A great many people, confronted with implementing diets of virtual life and death importance, labored with imagination and diligence to create recipes that would fill not only a nutritional need but an emotional one as well. Their empathy with the reader's problem and willingness to share the solution bespeak a motivation that goes far beyond any personal gain.

The same willingness to explain and assist was evident in the preparation of this book. The person who gave most generously of her time on book selection and terminology was consulting dietitian Patricia McNeece Kelly, R.D., of San Diego. Her enthusiasm, decisiveness, and clear perception of the needs of the reader were invaluable. She filled many gaps in the author's knowledge, and was instrumental in refining guidelines for a sound but practical book. I would like to express a special thanks to her for all of her help.

Ruth Shear Reznikoff, R.D., of the Heart Association of San Diego County, also willingly shared her expertise. Not only did she review all of the books and pamphlets considered for inclusion in the fat-controlled section, but she offered sensible advice for which I am very grateful.

It would be impossible to overstate the gratitude I owe to the many dietitians and public health nutritionists in San Diego and throughout the country who responded to the survey calling for recommended book titles. Their ideas substantially broadened the base of book selection, and their personal letters, which so often accompanied the returned survey forms, were a source of constant encouragement during a long and difficult job.

Two people who encouraged and advised me at the very outset of this project, and whom I wish to thank, are Wini Reuder McGuane, R.D., Past President of the San Diego District, California Dietetic Association, and Harriet E. Sankey, Managing Editor of the *Journal of the American Dietetic Association.*

The problem of how to handle books that had received both recommendations and nonrecommendations posed a real dilemma. Helen Denning Ullrich, R.D., Executive Director of the Society for Nutrition Education, suggested that books receiving a single nonrecommendation be dropped from consideration. My first reaction was that such standards of acceptance were too high. Nevertheless, I applied this rule. It soon became evident that the elimination of all weak links only strengthened the chain. In retrospect I see her admonition as the most valuable advice given on the formation of the book. Ms. Ullrich also must be thanked for recommending Particia McNeece Kelly to me, and for permitting me to use the library facilities of the *Journal of Nutrition Education* and the National Nutrition Education Clearing House in Berkeley, California.

As always, it was a pleasure to call upon the excellent resources and highly professional assistance so readily available at the San Diego Public Library and the Biomedical Library at the University of California, San Diego. A book of this nature, however, necessitated a search beyond these major sources. Among those in San Diego whom I would like to single out for thanks are Mildred Smith, R.D., of Mercy Hospital, Joanne Hill of the Dairy Council of California, and the librarians at the Thompson Medical Library at Balboa Naval Hospital, the San Diego County Library Reference Center, and the San Diego Medical Society-University Hospital Library.

Dozens of correspondents in the food industry, hospitals, health associations, universities, nutrition journals, and other institutions and businesses helped in countless ways. Every response was sincerely appreciated. Nor could this book have been done without the splendid cooperation of many publishers, large and small, who sent review copies and provided other essential information.

Recognition must be given to Jo-Ellen Schwartz Rudolf for the excellent job she did in indexing most of the recipes. Others who aided by their careful work in typing and proofreading include Marty Vaughn, Jake Hurtt Sabo, and Paula Yancy.

In conclusion, a great many people took their time to give me their best assistance or professional advice. Whether they are named here or not, I wish to thank all of them most sincerely for their unstinting encouragement and help.

Joan T. Casale
La Jolla, California

How to Use This Book

Diet Categories

Arrangement

The general diet categories in Parts I and II are identified by the letters A through O. The subdivisions bear a corresponding letter and are numbered consecutively under each general category. These letters and numbers are used throughout the text and in the subject index to refer to sections of the book.

The classification of diet categories and terminology follow *A Guide to Nutrition Terminology for Indexing and Retrieval* by E. Neige Todhunter, Ph.D. (U.S. Dept. HEW, 1970). Prepared under the auspices of the National Institutes of Health in cooperation with major national and international organizations engaged in nutrition programs and research, the scheme of classification presented is standard in the dietetic profession. Diets generally are classified according to the type of ingredient, or nutrient control desired. In other words, diet classification answers the question, "*Which* nutrient factor(s) must be controlled?" The question of *why* particular nutrients are controlled is left to the physician. The question of *how* nutrients are controlled and the resulting food made palatable—the essence of the diet itself—is the work of dietitians. Diets based on ingredient and nutrient control are covered in Part I, Therapeutic and Special Diets.

The major nutrient categories controlled by therapeutic diets are calories, carbohydrates, fats, minerals, and protein. Consistency (texture) may also be altered, by itself or in combination with nutrient control. Therapeutic diets based on modifications of these nutrient categories are the major divisions of Part I. The subdivisions—individual types of therapeutic diets such as calorie-restricted—depend on the *way* in which particular nutrients are controlled. Nutrients may be *increased*, as in high caloric diets; they may be *decreased*, as in calorie-restricted (low calorie) diets; or, they may be totally *eliminated*, as in gluten-restricted diets. At other times, nutrients must be present in certain *proportions* to other nutrients, as in the carefully balanced relationship of protein, fat, and carbohydrate in diabetic diets.

In the nutrient control classification system employed, a diet may be used for any number of reasons. Mineral modifications provide a good illustration of this flexibility. Copper-restricted diets are used only for a rare, hereditary disease. On the other hand, sodium-restricted diets may be prescribed for a potpourri of maladies, including congestive heart failure, toxemia in pregnancy, kidney disease, and hypertension. Perhaps new applications will be found for either copper-restricted or sodium-restricted diets, or old applications may be discontinued as other methods of treatment replace them. Or, minerals now regarded as innocuous may in the future be revealed as the source of some disease or malfunction, and will be entered under the Mineral Modifications heading. Thus, the system can readily accommodate a variety of changes in diet therapy. Since this book was written for lay persons, it is assumed that they already have received professional medical advice on their problem, and are simply seeking a way to cook around it.

A few changes have been made in Todhunter's scheme. Food Composition and Nutrition Education, two separate major categories, have been combined as a single heading; each subject, however, has its own subheading. The dietitians consulted have hesitated to place vegetarian diets in the Therapeutic and Special Diets category, so they are listed instead in Part II, Foods and Nutrition Education. In the interest of simplicity and space, most references to *fatty acids* (e.g. polyunsaturated fatty acids), have been shortened to the word *fat*.

One category of diet cookbooks and supplementary books does not concentrate on a single type of diet, but instead has anthologies of a number of different types of diets. These are collected under the Multiple Diets heading, and are the next to last entries in Part I, Therapeutic and Special Diets.

Diets for Special Conditions ordinarily would be classified separately from Therapeutic and Special Diets. However, the special conditions covered here—diets in pregnancy and lactation, youth diets, and geriatric diets—list only references to books classified in the preceding categories, and do not comprise a new body of annotated titles.

Since special and therapeutic diets, by definition, deviate in some way from a normal diet, it was decided to give at least token recognition to books on the basic principles and application of good nutrition. The books annotated in Part II, Foods and Nutrition Education range from elementary to fairly advanced expositions of the subject.

Food composition value books, which are applicable to a large number of diets, are presented under Food Composition and Values. A special set of cross-references following this section directs the reader to other sources of food composition values for *brand name* products. When food composition values apply primarily to a single type of diet, however, they appear in Part I grouped under supplementary books or brochures and product-related materials for the diet in question. For example, diabetic exchange lists are under Diabetic Diets, calorie counters are under Calorie-Restricted Diets. Cross-references are also given for applicable food composition values that can be found in books in other diet categories. The checklist following each annotation, of course, tells the reader which, if any, food value charts and tables are included in a specific book.

The suitability of specific, popular diets, especially in the area of weight loss, is a common concern for the nonprofessional. Evaluation of Popular Diets, which follows the section on Food Composition and Values, contains references to two books which critically evaluate, by name, many of the most popularly known diets.

Originally, vegetarian diets had not been considered for inclusion in this book. Many dietitians, however, urged the author to cover this subject since even vegetarians of long standing often are unaware of the critical importance of applying the most recent discoveries in vegetarian nutrition. Moreover, what began largely as a philosophical, religious, or political option, now is being imposed as a personal economic necessity. Both cookbooks and supplementary books have been annotated. Orthodox acceptance of *proper* vegetarian diets is attested to by the fact that several outstanding titles on the subject are published by the American Dietetic Association.

Terminology

A brief introductory statement about the diet and related terminology is given at the beginning of each diet category in the annotated bibliography. Because the nutrition vocabulary of the typical nonprofessional is so imprecise, there has been no choice but to employ accepted professional terminology in diet category headings, and to provide cross-references from the everyday terms that most people use. The quickest way to locate entries for a particular type of diet is to consult the Subject Index, which has been designed to bridge the gap between nonprofessional and professional usage.

The Annotated Bibliography

Arrangement

Books are listed in order of preference within each diet category. In deciding the order of listings, each recommendation or book review by a dietitian counted as one vote. A "no" vote or "nonrecommendation" automatically excluded the book from consideration (with only one or two exceptions). Books that received the same number of recommendations, are arranged alphabetically by author, except when one author is a dietitian, in which case that book is placed first.

The subheadings within the diet categories are: (1) cookbooks, (2) supplementary books, (3) brochures and product-related materials, (4) foreign language materials, and (5) periodicals. Not all of the diets have listings under each of the five subheadings; wherever possible cross-references have been inserted under these headings, if information can be found elsewhere in the book.

Each book has an entry number, determined by the order in which it appears in *The Diet Food Finder*, which is used for cross-references and as a reference number in the Recipe Indexes.

If a book's recipes are included in a recipe index, the name of the recipe index, e.g., Calorie-restricted, or Sodium-restricted, etc., appears directly under the bibliographic data for that book. A book may be included in more than one recipe index.

Content

The essential bibliographical information in the citation is much the same as that found in any such listing. Whenever possible, however, the postage paid price for a single copy is included. Because so many of the books are published by dietetic associations, hospitals, health service groups, and small publishers who operate outside normal book distribution channels, full addresses for ordering books are included in Appendix 1: Directory of Publishers.

Trusting in the good judgement of those who recommended the books, it is assumed that all the books are nutritionally sound. The annotations, therefore, make no men-tion of this topic, but attempt to describe the contents of each book and its general usefulness to the average, nonprofessional cook. Some of the qualities commented upon include:

The book's history, or qualifications of the author, if pertinent.

How well the title describes the contents (especially in the fat-controlled category).

Particularly attractive or well-organized books (or the opposite).

Comparisons with other books in the same category.

The extent of supplementary information, such as tables, charts, cooking tips, shopping advice, etc.

The inclusion of exercise programs.

Particular emphasis on ethnic or national cookery.

The scope and general character of the recipes.

Special features or information, presented in summary form as a list following the text of the annotations (see full explanation given under the heading "Master Checklist" at the end of this section).

Cross-References

More recipes and supplementary information on specific diets, or on combinations of diets, can be found by using the system of cross-references, which are located either at the end of the introductory statement concerning a particular diet category, or directly following the subheadings: cookbooks, supplementary books, and foreign language materials. As noted earlier, many diets are given excellent coverage in the multiple diet books; such information is always included in the cross-references.

Cross-references to either additional recipes or supplementary information give not only entry numbers, but the diet categories in which the books are annotated. For additional sodium-restricted recipes, for example, the reader is referred to both the fat-controlled and multiple diet books. Cross-references to supplementary information on sodium-restricted diets include entry numbers for books listed under calorie-restricted, fat-controlled, fat-restricted, and vegetarian diets. Thus, the person who must follow both a sodium-restricted and fat-restricted diet, or the vegetarian who needs advice on a sodium-restricted diet, can easily locate any available information.

The Recipe Indexes

The Recipe Indexes are arranged alphabetically, according to diet category, from Allergy Diets through Sodium-Restricted Diets. These indexes should enable the reader to easily find suitable recipes for old favorites, or for new foods that conform to the limitations imposed by any of ten different diets.

To locate the recipe for a particular food, e.g., bread for a protein-restricted diet, first turn to the appropriate recipe index, in this case the Protein-restricted Recipe Index. The *Bread* entry lists eight reference numbers: 157, 158, 163, etc. These numbers are the entry numbers for the annotated bibliography, and tell the reader in which books recipes for protein-restricted bread can be found. Subentries under protein-restricted *Bread* include two references to "low sodium bread," and one each for "low electrolyte bread" and "Swedish rye bread." Using this series of entries as an illustration, it should be pointed out that some of the simple *bread* entries may indeed also be "low sodium" or "low electrolyte" bread, in addition, of course, to the primary classification of protein-restricted (low protein). The description used in the Recipe Indexes rarely ventures beyond the cookbook author's own classification. To follow a more liberal policy of classification would have meant analyzing each of the 15,000 recipes indexed.

To facilitate checking citations referred to by the entry numbers in the Recipe Indexes, a list of book titles, arranged by entry number, directly follows the Recipe Indexes. The reader, therefore, will not have to page through all the annotations in order to identify a recipe source. At the beginning of each individual recipe index numbers of all recipe sources cited in that index are given.

Readers should check off those books in their own collections, or note where others can be consulted. If one's collection does not include all of the books indexed, the following are some suggested recipe sources:

1. Public libraries, applied sciences section.

2. Utility companies, home economist or dietitian.

3. College or university libraries, applied sciences section.

4. Health associations, such as the local chapter of the American Heart Association, the American Diabetes Association, or the Kidney Foundation; dietitian or home economist.

5. Dial-a-Dietitian, a service of local districts of state dietetic associations, available in many cities. Check the telephone directory.

At times the reader must be patient in locating a recipe in the recommended cookbook or pamphlet. Some of the smaller books and pamphlets do not contain indexes at all, and some of the larger books do not index recipes by any conventional standards. Recipes may be classified by adjectives or other modifiers, or dumped under imaginatively contrived headings. (Sources so frustrating to use might well have been eliminated from the recipe indexes, but it was decided by the author that any temporary inconvenience would be outweighed by the advantage of having available every recipe that could possibly assist the dieter.)

This discussion is not meant to discourage the reader, but only to pass along a few tips for using poorly indexed cookbooks. For example, an entry in the Recipe Index that reads, *Cake, chocolate, fluffy* may not read that way in the source cited. If it doesn't, the reader would be wise to look under "chocolate," and even "fluffy." Catchall headings, such as "desserts," are other places that should be checked. An attempt has been made to provide a *link word* between every entry in *The Diet Food Finder's* Recipe Indexes and the indexes of the sources cited.

Whenever possible all recipes in recommended cookbooks are included in that diet's recipe index. In a few categories, such as fat-controlled diets, some books at the lower end of the preference list were not included since there were more than enough recipes available. When a choice was made, consideration was given to recipes with quantitative ingredient control information, and to recipe collections that would add to the variety of foods indexed.

The Allergy Recipe Index is divided into 11 subcategories. In all there are six different allergy categories that include egg-free recipes, six for milk-free, and eight for wheat-free recipes. Not all of these will be appropriate for the person who is allergic to only one ingredient, but they should be considered as many of them are suitable for several purposes.

Readers looking for gluten-restricted recipes should check the main Gluten-Restricted Recipe Index, and four indexes under the Allergy Recipe Index; these include gluten-restriction in combination with other types of ingredient control.

Fat-controlled diets seemed to offer a few pitfalls. Many so-called "low cholesterol" recipes for liver, for example, turned out to be simply liver *without* bacon! Upon the advice of Ruth Shear Reznikoff, R.D., no liver recipes were included in the Fat-Controlled Recipe Index, and readers are cautioned to use shellfish recipes in moderation. As far as was possible, recipes with three or four whole eggs also were omitted from this index.

Other Features

Bibliography

Included here is a list of printed sources used in finding and evaluating books. One state's health department submitted a very helpful annotated book list, but asked not to be indentified.

Directory of Publishers

Alphabetical by publisher' last names, this directory (Appendix 1) also lists the entry numbers of books with their publisher.

Mail-Order Sources for Special Dietary Foods

Sources for special dietary foods that can be obtained by retail mail order are given in Appendix 2. An alphabetically arranged list of names and addresses of suppliers which sell directly to consumers in retail quantities, notes the type of food products offered. Each retailer is assigned a letter, **A**, **B**, **C**, etc., which is used in the Ingredient Control Chart. The latter enables the reader to quickly ascertain which suppliers specialize in products with particular types of ingredient control, e.g., calorie-restricted, gluten-restricted, and sodium-restricted.

The Brand Name Availability List in Appendix 3 shows brand names of special dietary foods that are available by mail order, with the same letters **A**, **B**, **C**, etc. indicating suppliers that carry particular brands.

Since many special diet foods can be made "from scratch," a person who is willing to forego the convenience of buying prepared foods should check the appropriate recipe index to see if the desired food can be prepared at home.

Indexes

The Diet Food Finder contains an Author Index, Title Index, and a Subject Index. All numbers used in these indexes refer to the entry numbers of the annotated bibliography.

The Author Index should be of assistance in evaluating new diet cookbooks, since it it likely that future books written by authors included in *The Diet Food Finder* will follow the same standards with regard to basic nutrition and ingredient control.

The Subject Index provides an essential link between nonprofessional and professional terminology. An attempt has been made to list all commonly known labels for therapeutic diets, and to direct the reader from these popular designations to the correct professional terms and subsequent annotations. The "low cholesterol" entry refers the reader to fat-controlled diets; "salt-free," "salt-poor," "low salt," and "low sodium" all refer to sodium-restricted diets; "low blood sugar" refers to hypoglycemia diets. Numbers in the Subject Index indicate entry numbers of the book annotations.

As an added function, the Subject Index includes references to many well-known diets that have *not* been included in this book, but which have been reviewed by dietitians in books annotated in *The Diet Food Finder*. Entries for these diets, such as the Air Force Diet, Dr. Atkins's Diet Revolution, and the Bananas and Skim Milk Diet, direct the reader to the Evaluation of Popular Diets where materials covering these diets are listed. The Subject Index also points out books that emphasize ethnic or national cookery, such as Mexican, French, Japanese, Jewish, and materials in foreign languages, such as Chinese, French, Spanish. Other references note books that include information on budget cookery, camping, exercises, textured vegetable protein, and travel information.

Master Checklist

As in any specialized collection, certain features tend to recur with great frequency. To avoid lengthy and repetitious narratives in the annotations, a master checklist of some 80 features was drawn up and those appearing in each title are listed at the end of the annotation. In this way the reader can see at once whether or not a book has height/weight charts, gives tips on packed lunches, or includes suggestions for children's diets. The number of recipes, and exactly what information is given with each recipe—calories, diabetic exchanges, milligrams of sodium, etc.—also can be determined with ease.

Some explanatory notes are given on the Master Checklist itself, but a few others are in order:

1. All measurements for nutrient content in charts, tables, and recipes, unless otherwise noted, are given in metric units.

2. Entries under Food Value Charts and Tables list only calcium, potassium, and sodium as individual minerals shown in a book's charts. Other minerals, such as iron, may be given separately in the books themselves, but are presented in the checklist under the umbrella term, "vitamins/minerals." Mineral content of foods is readily available in Food Composition and Value books, and would require considerable space to repeat in dozens of checklists. Exceptions have been made for certain books under Multiple Diets and Food Composition and Values.

3. Comparable nutritional information regarding recipes, e.g., milligrams of calcium, copper, iron, sodium, etc., is given in detail under the recipe entry in each book's checklist, since such information is not otherwise available without laborious research and tedious mathematical calculations.

4. Diabetic exchanges once were the only "exchanges," but since 11 different types of exchange lists are utilized in books annotated in *The Diet Food Finder*, an explanation of this concept is appropriate. All exchange list systems are governed by the same principle, and a caloric exchange system used for calorie-restricted diets will serve as a typical example.

Measured portions of food having approximately the same caloric and nutrient value (carbohydrate, fat, protein, vitamins, and minerals), and which therefore can be "exchanged," are grouped into different categories or "exchange lists": bread, fat, fruit, meat, milk, two types of vegetables, and a "free" list of foods and seasonings of negligible food value. The dieter is assigned a certain number of exchanges from each list for each meal per day, instead of being assigned a certain number of calories. For example, the meat (protein) exchange list for a calorie-restricted diet gives one ounce of Swiss cheese, one egg, three medium sardines, one frankfurter, two tablespoons of peanut butter, or one ounce of cooked beef, as equivalent or interchangeable foods. Breakfast for a 1000-calorie per day diet should consist of the following exchanges: one meat, one bread, one fruit, one-half milk, and one fat, plus moderate use of the "as desired" vegetable group and of the free list. Although a soft-boiled egg might be a typical choice for the breakfast "meat" exchange, any of the other equivalent foods from the meat exchange list could be substituted.

Since therapeutic diets focus on different nutrients which are of particular importance, exchange lists vary. Exchanges for protein-restricted diets take into account both the quantity and quality of protein; the exchanges are assigned in lieu of a specific number of grams of protein. Sodium exchanges emphasize low sodium foods, and exchanges are used instead of having an individual calculate the milligrams of sodium in food portions.

Dieters benefit from exchange systems in two ways. First, the proper type and amount of nutrients can be regulated without having to memorize enormous lists of food portions and nutrient values. Second, by drawing from *all* the assigned exchanged lists, the dieter gets a properly balanced diet.

Exchange systems are comparable to automatic transmission in automobiles as opposed to the "stick shift" method of calculating grams, milligrams, and calories. Both accomplish the same thing. Naturally, the simpler, more convenient way is preferred by most people. But, in dieting as in driving, the option remains for employing the "old fashioned" method that offers greater selectivity and control, plus the satisfaction of being a purist.

Following is the Master Checklist:

beverages, alcoholic
brand name information
canning
convenience foods (prepared foods,
    mixes, etc. discussed in text
    and/or used in recipes)
entertaining
food lists
  permitted
  restricted
food value charts & tables (information
    concerning the following)
  amino acids (milligrams)
  brand name products
  calcium
  caloric exchanges
  calories (kilocalories)
  carbohydrate (grams)
  cholesterol (milligrams)

food value charts & tables (cont.)
  cholesterol lowering exchanges
  diabetic exchanges
  fat (if no further designation, under-
    stood to mean total amount of
    fat or fatty acids, expressed in
    grams)
    total (grams)
  monounsaturated/oleic (may be
    given as "monounsaturated fat"
    or as "oleic acid," expressed
    in grams)
  polyunsaturated/linoleic (may be
    given as "polyunsaturated fat"
    or as "linoleic acid," expressed
    in grams)
    saturated (grams)
  fat exchanges
  ketogenic exchanges

food value charts & tables (cont.)
   phenylalanine (milligrams)
   phenylalanine exchanges
   potassium (milligrams)
   potassium exchanges
   protein (grams)
   protein exchanges
   sodium (milligrams)
   sodium exchanges
   triglyceride lowering exchanges
   vitamins/minerals (various vitamins
      and/or minerals, aside from cal-
      cium, potassium and sodium,
      which have individual listings)
freezing
glossary
guest dining (eating in another's home)
height/weight charts
lunches, packed
meal plans (general dietary scheme
      which suggests types of foods,
      rather than specific foods or
      dishes)
measurements: metric/household (con-
      version tables)
menus, everyday/holiday
minimum daily requirements
recipes (approximate total number;
      information listed below is given
      with each recipe)
   calcium (milligrams)
   caloric exchanges
   calories (kilocalories)
   carbohydrate (grams)
   casserole dish
   cholesterol (milligrams)
   copper (milligrams)
   diabetic exchanges

recipes (cont.)
   diet categories (specifically noted
      on recipe as opposed to reliance
      on chapter heading, book title,
      etc.)
   fat (if no further designation, under-
      stood to mean total amount of
      fat or fatty acids)
    total (grams)
    monounsaturated/oleic (grams)
    polyunsaturated/linoleic (grams)
    saturated (grams)
    long-chain triglycerides (grams)
    medium-chain triglycerides (grams)
   fat exchanges
   fluid (cubic centimeters)
   freezes (suitable for storage in freezer)
   glucose, total available (grams)
   iron (milligrams)
   magnesium (milligrams)
   oil (teaspoons)
   phenylalanine (milligrams)
   phenylalanine exchanges
   potassium (milligrams)
   protein (grams)
   protein exchanges
   serving (or yield or recipe)
   sodium (milligrams)
   sodium exchanges
recommended dietary allowances
references/bibliography (sources used
      and/or suggested reading list)
restaurant dining
seasonings (extensive discussion or list
      of)
sweeteners, artificial (discussion or
      guidelines for use of)
youth diets (infants through teens)

I.

THERAPEUTIC AND SPECIAL DIETS

A.
Allergy Diets

Allergy diets are prescribed for persons who are hypersensitive to a substance in food that normally is innocuous to the average person when taken in similar amounts. A variety of foods can trigger allergic reactions.

Allergy cookbooks generally are organized in two different ways. The first method is diagnostic, and presents "elimination diets," or a systematic program of eliminating all potentially offensive foods. Then, one new food at a time is added to the diet in an attempt to discover which, if any, food causes an allergic reaction. Only a few books are organized primarily to meet this need, and they are grouped apart under the heading, Diagnostic Allergy Elimination Diets (*see* A–1). Most of the material contained in these books, however, could be used in the second category of allergy cookbooks.

The second type of allergy cookbook is therapeutic, and assumes that the individual already knows which ingredients cause allergic reactions. Recipes and menus are planned to avoid the offensive ingredients. Since the individual must deal with the food allergy on a continuing basis—sometimes for an entire lifetime—this type of book comprises most of the literature in allergy cookery.

Many allergy cookbooks include recipes for gluten-restricted diets. For all practical purposes, the term "gluten-free" means barley-, oat-, rye-, and wheat-free. Therefore, readers can use gluten-free recipes in allergy cookbooks or those in gluten-restricted diet cookbooks if their allergies involve barley, oats, rye, or wheat.

To help readers who would like a complete rundown of all available recipe sources for a particular type of food allergy, the chart in Figure 1 shows all appropriate books and brochures, and the types of recipes they contain. Allergy diets that are shaded on the chart indicate that *The Diet Food Finder* contains a recipe index for the ingredient control specified. Note that gluten-free recipes are barley-, oat-, rye-, and wheat-free. More comprehensive sources of gluten-free recipes are found in Gluten-Restricted Diets (*see* H–1).

For supplementary information on diagnostic allergy elimination diets *see* Multiple diets: 171.

For supplementary information on therapeutic allergy diets *see* Gluten-restricted diets: 148; Food composition and values: 181.

For foreign language material on therapeutic allergy diets *see* Gluten-restricted diets: 152, 153.

Figure 1 presents a table of sources for ingredient-controlled recipes. Books are listed in rows; diet (free-from) categories are columns.

Source	cereal-free	cereal, egg, milk-free	egg-free	egg, gluten-free	egg, gluten, milk-free	egg, gluten, milk, wheat-free	egg, gluten, wheat-free	egg, milk-free	egg, milk, wheat-free	egg, wheat-free	galactose-free	gluten-free	gluten, milk-free	gluten, milk, wheat-free	gluten, wheat-free	milk-free	milk-wheat-free	wheat-free
1 ALLERGY COOKING. Conrad		✓							✓									
2 ELIMINATION DIETS. Rowe	✓																	✓
3 ALLERGY RECIPES. American Dietetic Assn.			✓	✓			✓	✓	✓	✓				✓	✓	✓		✓
4 THE EGGLESS COOKBOOK. Sattler			✓		✓			✓										
5 CREATIVE COOKING WITHOUT WHEAT, MILK AND EGGS. Shattuck			✓	✓	✓	✓	✓	✓	✓	✓		✓	✓	✓	✓	✓		✓
6 BAKING FOR PEOPLE WITH FOOD ALLERGIES. U.S. Dept. Agriculture									✓	✓						✓		
7 GOOD RECIPES TO BRIGHTEN THE ALLERGY DIET. Best Foods			✓			✓	✓	✓	✓	✓					✓	✓	✓	✓
8 125 GREAT RECIPES FOR ALLERGY DIETS. Good Housekeeping			✓			✓		✓	✓	✓				✓			✓	✓
9 ALLERGY RECIPES FROM THE BLUE FLAME KITCHEN. Metropolitan Utilities District								✓	✓					✓	✓			✓
10 MISS FLUFFY'S TASTY RICE RECIPES FOR THOSE WITH ALLERGIES. Rice Council of America			✓					✓	✓									✓
11 GOOD EATING FOR THE MILK-SENSITIVE PERSON. Ross Laboratories									✓								✓	
58 DIET MANAGEMENT FOR ULCERATIVE COLITIS. Hanson									✓									
169 GOOD HOUSEKEEPING COOKBOOK FOR CALORIE WATCHERS. Schoenberg						✓		✓	✓	✓				✓	✓		✓	
171 FOOD, NUTRITION, & DIET THERAPY. Krause and Hunscher			✓					✓	✓	✓	✓				✓		✓	✓

Figure 1. Sources for ingredient-controlled recipes.

A-1. Diagnostic Allergy Elimination Diets

Cookbooks

1 Conrad, Marion L. ALLERGY COOKING. Thomas Y. Crowell, 1960. 380 pp. index. hard $6.50; Pyramid, paper $.95.
Recipe Index: Allergy.

First published in 1955, this book is a classic in allergy cookery. The author is a dietitian who suffered a number of illnesses found to be caused by food allergies. With the help of the noted allergist, Dr. Albert H. Rowe, she developed basic menus, diets and recipes to cope with her own problems, in addition to those of her family and patients. The introductory chapters of the book cover family adjustments to an allergy diet, illness, picnics, camping and pack trips, parties, babies' and children's allergies, losing and gaining weight, and advice to older adults. The menus and recipes are grouped under seven different diet headings. The basic elimination diet, which is cereal-, egg-, and milk-free, comprises more than 550 of the book's 750 recipes. The six remaining diets are classified as basic plus egg, basic plus milk, basic plus cereal, etc. A week's menus are provided for each variation of the basic diet. The large recipe collection is very strong in American cookery, and offers an amazing variety of foods within the strict limitations of no cereal, egg, or milk. To insure variety in the diet, the author lists meats, potatoes, fruits, and vegetables that can be rotated in daily menus. With the author's positive outlook, the excellent recipe collection, and good organization, it is no wonder that the book has been in print for two decades. Only the basic diet is included in the Recipe Index as an egg-, milk-, and wheat-free diet.

bibliography	guest dining	recipes: 750
canning	lunches, packed	servings
entertaining	meal plans	restaurant dining
food value charts & tables	menus: everyday, holiday	youth diets
protein		
vitamins/minerals		

2 Rowe, Albert, Jr., M.D., and Sinclair. Colin E., M.D. THE ELIMINATION DIETS. Lea & Febiger, 1972. 38 pp. paper $.50(order from Holmes Book Co.)
Recipe Index: Allergy.

This booklet is a reprint from two books by Dr. Rowe, Jr. and his late father: *Food Allergy* and *The Elimination Diets and the Patient's Allergies*. The editorial approach is that of advice to the prescribing physician. Although some of the material is on a higher technical level than average, the information about food is easily understood. Two cereal-free elimination diets, a fruit-free elimination diet, a cereal-free elimination diet for infants, and a minimal fruit-free elimination diet are included. The recipes are for cereal-free elimination diets. The cereal-free recipes are included in the Recipe Index under wheat-free.

brand name information	lunches, packed	recipes: 45
food lists	meal plans	references
permitted	menus: everyday	youth diets

A-2. Therapeutic Allergy Diets

Cookbooks

For additional therapeutic allergy diet recipes *see* Ulcerative colitis diets: 58; Gluten-restricted diets: 145, 146, 147, 149, 150, 151; Multiple diets: 169, 171.

3 American Dietetic Assn. ALLERGY RECIPES. 1969. 64 pp. paper $1.
Recipe Index: Allergy.

Perhaps the diet cookbook with the greatest longevity, the American Dietetic Association's allergy recipe collection has been revised and expanded many times since its inception in 1933. The current edition recognizes that most homemakers have neither the time nor the desire to prepare every dish from scratch, and makes liberal use of convenience foods in the recipes. Clear and direct, it meets the objectives set forth in the foreword: recipes that can be prepared quickly, appeal to both children and adults, and be accepted by nonallergic members of the family. The introductory sections present good ideas for helping children to cope with their food limitations, and tips for baking with nonwheat flours. Most of the recipes are for baked goods, and all are truly modifications of recipes that usually require wheat, milk, or eggs. Many books include scores of recipes for ingredient-"free" recipes when the ingredient in question normally isn't used anyway. In place of an index, each section has its own semi-indexed table of contents. Since it is not located in the back of the book, but preceding each section, the first impression (which is a false one) is that there is no way to locate particular recipes.

brand name information
convenience foods
food lists
   restricted

recipes: 130
  servings
references
youth diets

4 Sattler, Helen Roney. THE EGGLESS COOKBOOK. Barnes & Co., 1972. 155 pp. index. hard $6.95.
Recipe Index: Allergy.

The author, who is a writer of children's books, developed this cookbook in 15 years of collecting and perfecting eggless recipes, first for her children who are allergic to eggs and later for her husband, who had been placed on a low-cholesterol diet. Many of the recipes are also milk-free; these are indicated by an asterisk in both the recipe title and the index. Keeping the busy cook in mind, the author utilizes brand name mixes and other convenience foods whenever possible. Her concern that children on egg-free diets not miss any of the fun of traditional holidays shows in the inclusion of two recipes for Easter "eggs" that can be colored and eaten. The recipe collection concentrates primarily on desserts, with a wide selection of cakes, icings, cookies, candies, ice creams and sherbets, puddings, and pies. Breakfast dishes, such as pancakes and waffles, are covered, as well as salad dressings and main dishes. A number of good tips on allergy cooking are provided. An unusual table gives English and American equivalents of household measurements.

brand name information
convenience foods

recipes: 220
  diet categories
  servings

5 Shattuck, Ruth R. CREATIVE COOKING WITHOUT WHEAT, MILK AND EGGS. Barnes & Co., 1974. 188 pp. index. hard $6.95.
Recipe Index: Allergy*; Gluten-restricted.

A well-organized and thoughtful cookbook, this title is the work of a dietitian who has spent 30 years preparing meals for her allergic husband and nonallergic children. General kitchen tips for cooking without eggs, milk, and wheat are given in the introduction, along with a chart showing the English (British) equivalents for household measurements. The use of carob in place of chocolate is also discussed. Interspersed with the recipes are countless suggestions for getting the best results under often difficult circumstances, and one gets a definite impression that the author really worked to make her recipes succeed. The recipes are divided into three main sections: breads and desserts (including cookies, pastries, frozen desserts, and sauces); fish and meats; and vegetables and soups. The baked goods section comprises the bulk of the recipe collection. Besides egg-, milk-, and wheat-free recipes, many are also gluten-free. One chapter title indicates that low-fat recipes are included, and although this is true, such ingredient control is not noted on the recipes themselves.

convenience foods
food value charts & tables
  protein

recipes: 275
  diet categories
  servings

Brochures and Product-Related Materials

6 U.S. Dept. of Agriculture. BAKING FOR PEOPLE WITH FOOD ALLER-GIES. Home and Garden Bulletin No. 147. 1968. 12 pp. index. paper $.10.
Recipe Index: Allergy.

Recipes include muffins, crackers, cakes, cookies, and pie crusts. Ingredient control categories are indicated on recipes and in the index.

recipes: 15
  diet categories
  servings

7 Best Foods. GOOD RECIPES TO BRIGHTEN THE ALLERGY DIET. single-page folder. free.
Recipe Index: Allergy.

This booklet contains mostly dessert recipes, including candy, cake, pudding, and pie, using the manufacturer's brand name products.

brand name information
recipes: 20
  servings

---

*All wheat-free allergy recipes from Shattuck's text were given the additional label of "gluten-free" in her index. Since the information in her index had to be used when preparing the various Recipe Indexes for *The Diet Food Finder*, this editorial anomaly meant that all wheat-free allergy recipes from *book 5* had to be classified in Recipe Index categories that are combinations of gluten-free and wheat-free. For an explanation of interchanging wheat-free and gluten-free recipes, see Allergy Diets, Part I-A.

8 Good Housekeeping. 125 GREAT RECIPES FOR ALLERGY DIETS. Hearst, 1967. 43 pp. paper $.50 prepaid.
Recipe Index: Allergy.

This substantial and varied collection includes mainly baked goods, but also covers main dishes and casseroles, vegetables, soups, sauces, and salad dressings. The book is greatly handicapped by the lack of an index, which is a necessity in any recipe collection of this size.

convenience foods
recipes: 125
   diet categories
   servings

9 Metropolitan Utilities District. ALLERGY RECIPES FROM THE BLUE FLAME KITCHEN. 1963. 37 pp. paper $.50.
Recipe Index: Allergy.

In addition to the usual emphasis on baked goods, this booklet includes many casserole dishes. A good table of contents and clearly defined chapters help the cook to locate recipes. Good tips are given for allergy cookery.

recipes: 65
   servings

10 Rice Council of America. MISS FLUFFY'S TASTY RICE RECIPES—FOR THOSE WITH ALLERGIES. single-page folder. free.
Recipe Index: Allergy.

This simple folder contains an interesting collection of casserole, dessert, and breakfast dishes.

recipes: 30
   servings

11 Ross Laboratories. GOOD EATING FOR THE MILK-SENSITIVE PERSON: A SELECTION OF APPETIZING RECIPES MADE WITH SIMILAC® ISOMIL® CONCENTRATED LIQUID. 1969. 22 pp. illus. paper. free.
Recipe Index: Allergy.

A varied selection of recipes using the manufacturer's product, this booklet includes recipes for beverages, puddings, soups, sauces, main courses, and desserts.

recipes: 40
   diet categories
   servings

B.
Caloric Modifications

B-1. Calorie-Restricted Diets

To the average person, the word "diet" usually means a low-calorie diet for weight reduction. It also implies a magical solution for overweight. Alas, there is none. Calorie-restricted diets, which modify a normal diet pattern by reducing caloric intake and maintaining mineral and vitamin intake, are the only ones recommended by dietitians for safe and effective weight control. Only sound cookbooks, calorie counters, and motivational guides are included in this chapter. Many nonrecommended diets, and a few which have been approved, are covered in Part II-M, Evaluation of Popular Diets.

Calorie-restricted diets are presented either by the universally known method of counting calories (actually kilocalories, or units of 1000 calories) or by the more recently adopted exchange system that has been popularized by weight reduction clinics and some cookbooks. As noted in the section entitled "How to Use This Book," the exchange system provides an easier way to count calories and assures nutritional balance.

For books using number of calories in each recipe *see* 13, 14, 15, 17, 18, 19, 23, 24, 25, 35, 44, 47, 52.

For books using caloric exchanges in each recipe *see* 12, 20, 21, 22, 26.

For foreign language materials on calorie-restricted diets *see* Fat-controlled diets: 83; Diabetic diets: 137.

Cookbooks

For additional calorie-restricted recipes *see* Fiber-restricted diets: 57; Fat-controlled diets: 59, 62, 69, 77, 83; Fat-restricted diets: 86; Sodium-restricted: 92; Diabetic diets: 108; Multiple diets: 167, 168, 169, 170, 171; Nonprofessional nutrition education: 185.

12 Better Homes & Gardens. EAT & STAY SLIM. Meredith, 1968. 96 pp. index. illus. hard $1.95.
Recipe Index: Calorie-restricted; Diabetic.

This appealing cookbook is the most popular one on weight reduction among the dietitians surveyed. The introductory chapters cover sensible weight control, fallacies about reducing, figuring caloric needs, and the requirements of safe reducing. Instead of the traditional method of counting calories, the book effectively utilizes a color-coded caloric exchange system similar to the exchange system designed to simplify diabetic diets. In fact, many dietitians recommend this as a diabetic cookbook. Measured portions of foods that are equivalent in calories and nutrients are grouped together in exchange lists. The color coding system (yellow for fat exchanges, red for meat, etc.), used in all the menus, meal plans, recipes, snacks, and lunches, enables the reader to visualize immediately the limits of the meal without totaling calories. Of the several books reviewed in this category that employ a caloric exchange system, this one by far makes the most lucid presentation of the concept. Menus are included for 1000, 1200, and 1500 calorie diets. Although the recipe collection is not a large one, it emphasizes home-style American food from appetizers through desserts. The chapter on eating out is better than average, and the book provides clip-out food exchange lists. Photo-illustrated exercises for men and women complete the book.

beverages, alcoholic	height/weight charts	recipes: 80
convenience foods	lunches, packed	caloric exchanges
food value charts & tables	meal plans	servings
caloric exchanges	menus: everyday	restaurant dining
guest dining		seasonings

13 Jolliffe, Norman, M.D. REDUCE AND STAY REDUCED ON THE PRUDENT DIET. Simon & Schuster, 1963. 252 pp. index. illus. hard $4.95.
Recipe Index: Calorie-restricted.

The third edition of this classic book is highly recommended by established nutrition reviewers as a practical guide to reducing weight and altering eating habits with a "prudent diet" calculated to lower blood cholesterol. The author was director, Bureau of Nutrition, Department of Health, City of New York, from 1949 until his death in 1961. During that time he initiated a series of nutrition and obesity clinics to test and confirm the principles set forth in this book. The recipe collection is brief, and offers a few selections in each of the standard cookery categories, such as appetizers, soups, main dishes, etc. Nonetheless, this title is included in the cookbook category because of its popularity among dietitians and for the wealth of detailed instructions on diet plans. The author urges the dieter to understand basic concepts of nutrition in order to carry out a sensible and effective program of weight reduction. The first part of the book explains theories of appetite regulation (Dr. Jolliffe's "appestat"), reasons for reducing weight, and the mathematics of reduction. The practical application of diet theories fills the second half of the book: meal patterns for youths on diets of 1600, 1900, 2200, 2500, and 3000 calories and for adults at 600, 800, 1000, 1200, 1500, 1800, 2000, and 2500 calorie levels. Factual information on food values, menu modifications for low-sodium and emergency liquid diets, low-calorie cooking tips, recipes, and the "heart-saver diet for normal weight adults" are several of the main features. To a limited extent the concept of caloric exchanges is employed; foods are listed in groups equivalent in calories. The appendix contains a technical discussion of obesity and metabolism.

beverages, alcoholic	height/weight charts	restaurant dining
food value charts & tables	meal plans	seasonings
calories	recipes: 55	youth diets
	calories	

14 Better Homes & Gardens. CALORIE COUNTER'S COOK BOOK. Meredith, 1970. 96 pp. index. illus. hard $1.95; Bantam. 164 pp. index. paper $1.
Recipe Index: Calorie-restricted.

A colorful cookbook presenting a reasonably wide selection of recipes, this book guides the cook in planning calorie-controlled meals of all types, stressing inclusion of the basic four food groups. Beverage and sandwich recipes are included. Everyday menus outline 1000, 1200, 1500, and 1800 calorie diets. Seasoning guides suggest the best blend of flavors for fruits, meats, and vegetables. Clip-out calorie and cholesterol charts are included in the weight maintenance section. A major focus is on home entertainment. Menus and recipes are provided for weekend brunch, entertaining at lunch, family holiday dinners, and an evening buffet.

beverages, alcoholic	guest dining	recipes: 190
entertaining	lunches, packed	calories
food value charts & tables	meal plans	servings
calories	menus: everyday, holiday	restaurant dining
cholesterol		seasonings

15 Redbook's WISE WOMAN'S DIET AND EXERCISE BOOK. McCall, 1970. 119 pp. illus. hard $5.95.

This 1200 calorie diet and exercise program, first published in *Redbook* magazine, was planned with the assistance of Dr. George Christakis, former director, Bureau of Nutrition, New York City Department of Health. It combines sound nutrition with regular exercise; line drawings illustrate the recommended exercises. Menus and recipes acknowledge two eminently practical considerations in weight reduction: people's preference for favorite foods of their ethnic group and the fact that nearly half of American women eat lunch away from home five days a week. Reflecting the diverse background of New Yorkers (and of most Americans), the book provides menus and recipes for persons of German, French, Italian, Jewish, and Spanish descent. A 14-day diet program featuring American favorites includes both menus and recipes. Each workday menu lists two lunches: one to eat at home and one to pack and carry to the office or factory. In addition, a separate two-week summer reducing plan offers menus with seasonal fruits, vegetables, and picnic sandwiches.

height/weight charts	recipes: 70
lunches, packed	calories
menus: everyday, holiday	servings

16 Siegel, Murray J., and van Keuren, Dolores. THINK THIN MANUAL AND COOKBOOK. Paul S. Eriksson, 1971. 272 pp. index. hard $6.95.
Recipe Index: Calorie-restricted.

The Think Thin Manual section of the book, comprising nearly half the text, is aimed at changing one's thinking about food in order to alter and improve eating habits to achieve significant weight loss. Emphasis is placed on consuming three nutritionally balanced meals a day and on maintaining weight loss. Several chapters explain exactly how to cope with eating out and how to say no to excess food in nearly every conceivable business and social situation. At the same time, positive suggestions are made for Thanksgiving, Christmas, Easter, and Passover meals. Although it is not so labeled, the book employs a caloric equivalent or exchange system for meal planning and recipes. The broadly based recipe collection includes ingenious low-calorie imitations of many normally rich foods, such as pizza, mashed potatoes, and Danish pastry. A good index assures easy reference to the Think Thin Manual section, as well as to the recipes and menus.

entertaining	food value charts & tables	menus: everyday, holiday
food lists	caloric exchanges	recipes: 300
permitted	guest dining	servings
restricted	lunches, packed	restaurant dining

17 Heller, Ann Williams. EAT & GET SLIM COOKBOOK. Fawcett, 1973. 208 pp. index. paper $.95.

The author has written seven cookbooks and innumerable articles on food and nutrition for leading magazines. The introductory chapters outline programs for weight reduction on 1000, 1100, and 1500 calorie diets. Menus are based on the four seasons, year-round applicability, and holiday festivities. Although calorie counts are provided for recipes and in the appendix, the meal plans are so designed that the dieter can reduce with a minimum of daily calculations. This book differs from others in its attention to shopping. Practical information is provided for each section of the supermarket, including how much uncooked meat, fruit, or vegetables will yield a single serving. Another list indicates the size and amount of fresh fruits and vegetables that fit the diet plan. Cooking tips for controlling the caloric content of foods are provided. Especially helpful are the notations on each recipe for preparation and cooking time.

food lists	glossary	recipes: 150
permitted	height/weight charts	calories
restricted	meal plans	servings
food value charts & tables	menus: everyday, holiday	restaurant dining
calories		seasonings

18 Belinkie, Helen. THE NEW GOURMET IN THE LOW-CALORIE KITCHEN COOKBOOK. David McKay, 1971. 257 pp. index. hard $6.95; Avon. paper $.95. *Recipe Index:* Calorie-restricted.

A complete cookbook for low-calorie recipes, this is a revised edition of a book published in 1961, and lists Margaret May as a consulting dietitian. No artificial sweeteners are used in the recipes. Symbols indicate which recipes are suitable for freezing or for preparation as casserole dishes. The first group of recipes are low-calorie versions of basic sauces, gravies, salad dressings, whipped cream, and sour cream. The Favorite Dishes of Other Countries chapter gives a truly round-the-world sampling of foreign cuisine, and a chapter on entertaining presents drinks, main courses, hors d'oeuvres, and dinner party and luncheon menus. Even beyond this, the book lives up to its title with gourmet recipes from many lands. Less exalted fare is included as well. The reader should be cautioned that many recipes in the dessert and alcoholic beverage chapters call for the use of sugar, honey, or maple syrup "to taste." Yet, the same recipes show a specific number of calories per serving!

beverages, alcoholic	freezing	casserole dish
entertaining	menus: everyday	freezes
food value charts & tables	recipes: 400	servings
calories	calories	

19 Chapin, Suzy. THE ADJUSTABLE DIET COOKBOOK. Funk & Wagnalls, 1967. 346 pp. index. hard $5.95.

This book presents a 600 calorie diet, which many nutrition authorities regard as too low. The author, however, notes that the diet was designed for her elderly, sedentary mother. The "adjustable" part of the title indicates that the diet can be increased in caloric content to the higher values that are more often recommended. The recipes are appetizing and the variety good. They are not, however, gathered into the usual categories of appetizers, meats, vegetables, etc. Instead, the collection is divided into winter, spring, summer, and fall menu chapters. The introduction to each seasonal section lists the main dishes for dinner menus for six weeks. Complete daily menus for six weeks are interspersed with recipes. Since recipes are presented as they are needed in the daily menus, an appetizer, main dish, and dessert may appear on the same page. While adequate for locating specific recipes, the index could be improved with the use of broader entry headings and cross-indexing in view of the unorthodox recipe arrangement.

food value charts & tables	menus: everyday	servings
calories	recipes: 400	restaurant dining
lunches, packed	calories	

20 Gold, Ann, and Briller, Sara Welles. DIET WATCHERS GUIDE. Grosset & Dunlap, 1968. index. 126 pp. paper $1.25; Bantam. 157 pp. index. paper $.95. *Recipe Index:* Calorie-restricted.

The book's first author has a background in food catering, and is the founder of a group dieting program, Diet Watchers, Inc., which encourages gradual weight loss and the acquisition of new eating habits. The first half of the book encourages the reader to follow the prescribed eating plan, while advising against crash dieting and the pitfalls encountered by the typical dieter. The food plan is based on a caloric exchange system. Although the Los Angeles District of the California Dietetic Association recommends this diet for short-term use, it points out that difficulties could arise over a long period of time because iron is inadequately supplied (bread and cereal group servings are replaced with meat servings). (*See* p. 5 in entry 190.)

The remainder of the book contains a variety of recipes for breakfast, lunch, and dinner, with some imaginative low-calorie substitutes for normally rich desserts.

food lists	food value charts & tables	recipes: 100
permitted	caloric exchanges	caloric exchanges
restricted	guest dining	servings
	height/weight charts	restaurant dining
	menus: everyday	youth diets

21 Lindauer, Lois Lyons. IT'S IN TO BE THIN...THE DIET WORKSHOP WAY. Prentice-Hall, 1970. index. hard 225 pp. $6.95; Award. 219 pp. paper $.95. *Recipe Index:* Calorie-restricted.

Written by the director of the New York-based Diet Workshop and author of the syndicated newspaper column "It's In to Be Thin," this book contains an imaginative and appetizing recipe collection. According to the jacket, the recipes have been approved for balanced nutritional value by Morton B. Glenn, M.D., of the Board of Health Obesity Clinic of the City of New York. The introduction outlines procedures for weight reduction for women, men, and teenage girls and boys, with notes on maintaining weight reduction. The diet plan is based on caloric exchange values, but not all of the recipes list exchange equivalents. The recipes are organized into chapters based on breakfast, lunch, and dinner menus, with two or three recipes provided for each menu. (This atypical arrangement is similar to that found in Chapin's *Adjustable Diet Cookbook*.) A number of practical considerations are included: breakfast menus for both heavy and light eaters, menus and recipes for company dinners, tips on dining away from home, and a chapter on snacks.

entertaining	guest dining	recipes: 100
food lists	height/weight charts	caloric exchanges
permitted	lunches, packed	restaurant dining
restricted	meal plans	youth diets
	menus: everyday	

22 Nidetch, Jean. WEIGHT WATCHER'S® PROGRAM COOKBOOK. Hearthside Press, 1973. 320 pp. index. illus. hard $6.95.
Recipe Index: Calorie-restricted.

Compiled by the founder of a well-known weight reduction program, the inventive recipes in this new cookbook were contributed by Weight Watchers organizations across the United States. Because the diet plan, which is based on a system of caloric exchanges, was revised in 1972, the original *Weight Watchers® Cook Book* has been allowed to go out of print. The present title contains all new recipes, and includes nearly every type of dish from gefilte fish to tacos. Hardly a vegetable, fruit, or cut of meat is neglected; an entire chapter is reserved for liver recipes. Reflecting changes in the eating program, it utilizes formerly excluded foods, such as pasta, potatoes, and rice. The weight reduction program is one of 12 analyzed by the Los Angeles District, California Dietetic Association, and is recommended by it for its "nutritional adequacy and for the education in making wise food choices." (*See* p. 21 in entry 190.) Chapter divisions stress the inclusion of all basic food groups, so that such titles as "Bread and Cereals" and "Milk" are found rather than "Appetizers" or "Desserts." In addition to weight reduction meal plans for men, women, and youth, advice is given on "leveling," or losing the last 10 pounds, and on maintaining proper weight.

food lists	food value charts & tables	recipes: 510
permitted	caloric exchanges	caloric exchanges
restricted	height/weight charts	servings
	meal plans	seasonings
	menus: everyday	youth diets

23 PILLSBURY'S FAMILY WEIGHT CONTROL COOKBOOK. Pillsbury Publications, 1970. 144 pp. index. illus. hard $3.95.
Recipe Index: Calorie-restricted.

In an especially practical book for the beginning cook, Pillsbury presents a great deal of useful information on weight reduction, nutrition, and food handling in a bright, attractive format. Introductory chapters guide the reader through weight reduction goals, eating out, balanced nutrition, shopping, and the benefits of careful meal planning. At least one week's menus, with calorie counts, are listed for breakfast, lunch, and dinner, with the bonus of needed recipes for the dinner menus. While the rest of the book is divided into chapters on beverages, snacks (unusually enticing ideas), soups, main dishes, etc., the editors have managed to slip in comprehensive information on the selection and use of many vegetables and cuts of meat, listing the varieties available, amount to purchase, characteristics of desirable produce or meat cuts, methods of preparation, cooking time, vitamins, and recommended seasoning or flavor companions. Such information would benefit not only the novice but also the experienced cook who needs a reminder on the myriad uses of neglected or abused vegetables. On the subject of convenience foods, the book discusses ways of dressing up prepared soups.

convenience foods
entertaining
food value charts & tables
  calories

guest dining
height/weight charts
lunches, packed
menus: everyday

recipes: 260
  calories
  servings
restaurant dining
seasonings

24 Better Homes & Gardens. LOW-CALORIE DESSERTS. Meredith, 1972. 96 pp. index. illus. hard $1.95.
Recipe Index: Calorie-restricted; Diabetic.

This beautifully illustrated book includes every type of dessert: beverages, cakes, cookies, frozen, fruits, gelatins, pies, puddings, sauces, soufflés, and toppings. Special chapters are devoted to holiday and company desserts. Others that can be prepared in only a few minutes and some meant to serve only one or two persons are given. Sixteen recipes are included for diabetics, each listing the diabetic exchanges and gram weights, in addition to the number of calories. A brief section covers the basic four food groups. A uniquely helpful feature is a second table of contents printed inside the front cover that groups the recipes according to their caloric value: under 60 calories, under 100 calories, under 125 calories, or under 150 calories.

entertaining
food value charts & tables
  calories

menus: everyday
recipes: 190
  calories
  servings

25 Crocker, Betty. BETTY CROCKER'S LOW-CALORIE COOKBOOK. Golden Press, 1973. 77 pp. index. illus. hard $2.50.
Recipe Index: Calorie-restricted.

One of the most inviting diet cookbooks reviewed, this Betty Crocker title is highly practical without being the least bit formidable. Fresh, workable ideas for following a weight reduction program are listed in the introduction. For those who would rather not count calories, the book offers the option of a simplified caloric exchange program based on the number of servings of various food groups that are permitted each day. Innumerable time- and calorie-saving tips are printed as marginal notations, and for once a picture is worth a thousand words. Excellent color photographs show carefully limited portions of snacks and meals that are labeled with the number of calories in each. Thus, the illustrations educate readers to aspire to restricted portions, instead of tempting them with the unlimited quantities that subliminally are suggested in pictures of whole pies, casseroles, roasts, etc. The imaginative recipe collection utilizes prepared foods and mixes to a large extent, and selection centers on meats and main dishes, salads and vegetables, and desserts.

convenience foods
food lists
  permitted
  restricted

food value charts & tables
  calories
guest dining
lunches, packed
meal plans

menus: everyday; holiday
recipes: 120
  calories
  servings

26 Frances, Evan. LADIES' HOME JOURNAL FAMILY DIET BOOK. Macmillan, 1973. 294 pp. index. illus. hard $6.95.

With the theme of "one family, one menu," this book strives to make weight reduction easy and workable within the context of normal family meals, without the necessity for long hours devoted to special diet cookery. The program is based on a system of caloric exchanges. Recipes and menus are organized according to the four seasons of the year, and two week's menus for 1200 to 1400 calorie diets are provided for each season. A question-and-answer section introduces the book, and a well-illustrated chapter on exercises follows the food section. Advice for dressing in the most flattering way, and hints on avoiding the commonest causes of backsliding comprise another chapter. Unfortunately, the otherwise outstanding recipes are presented in narrative form as opposed to the standard method of listing ingredients in columns, and therefore are difficult to evaluate at a glance and to follow. In conjunction with the book's theme, each recipe carries a separate notation on the portion suitable for the dieting member of the family, and the exchange value is represented.

convenience foods	food value charts & tables	recipes: 370
food lists	caloric exchanges	caloric exchanges
permitted	height/weight charts	servings
restricted	lunches, packed	seasonings
	menus: everyday	sweeteners, artificial

Supplementary Books

For additional supplmentary information on calorie-restricted diets *see* Fat-controlled diets: 72; Sodium-restricted diets: 95; Diabetic diets: 114, 119, 123, 124, 135; Multiple diets: 171, 172; Food composition and values: 177, 178, 179, 180, 181; Nonprofessional nutrition education: 182, 183, 184, 186, 190, 191, 194, 197, 198; Vegetarian diets: 206, 207, 208.

27 Mayer, Jean, Ph.D., D.Sc. OVERWEIGHT: CAUSES, COST AND CONTROL. Prentice-Hall, 1968. 213 pp. index. illus. hard $5.95; paper $2.45.

One of the world's leading authorities on nutrition, Mayer is a professor of nutrition at Harvard University and has written hundreds of research articles and reviews in the field of nutrition. Developed from the author's articles in the *Atlantic Monthly, Harpers,* the *New York Times Sunday Magazine,* as well as more technical information published for general practitioners in postgraduate medicine, the book is written on a fairly technical level, and presents a comprehensive view of the many theoretical and practical facets of overweight.

beverages, alcoholic	fat: total	recommended dietary allow-
food value charts & tables	protein	ances (RDA)
calories	vitamins/minerals	references
		youth diets

28 Goodhart, Robert S., M.D. THE TEEN-AGER'S GUIDE TO DIET AND HEALTH. Prentice-Hall, 1964. 176 pp. index. illus. cloth $4.95.

The author is the president and scientific director of the National Vitamin Foundation, Inc. More than a simple advisory on weight reduction, this book is a guide to good nutrition, and covers food fallacies, physical fitness, and general hygiene. Recipes are limited to party fare. A few menus are given for 1000, 1200, 1500, and 1800 calorie weight reduction diets. High-calorie diets also are listed for those who wish to gain weight. The book's 1000 calorie diet is not approved by one reviewer because it may fail to meet adolescent growth needs; it is also pointed out that many nutrition authorities would disagree with the author's total prohibition of certain foods in attempting to control overweight or tooth decay.*

entertaining	height/weight charts	recommended dietary allow-
food value charts & tables	menus: every day	ances (RDA)
caloric exchanges	recipes: 20	youth diets
calories		

29 Danowski, T. S., M.D. SUSTAINED WEIGHT CONTROL. 2nd ed. F. A. Davis, 1973. 194 pp. index. paper $1.95.

A professor of medicine at the University of Pittsburgh, Danowski is also the author of a number of books on diabetes. The weight reduction message of this book is directed at the individual, and is highly recommended by several major reviewers. Only a small part of the book is devoted to food and cookery, since the author's primary purpose is to motivate the reader to reorient personality and behavior.

food lists	calories	protein
permitted	carbohydrates	sweeteners, artificial
restricted	cholesterol	youth diets
food value charts & tables	fat: total	
brand name products		

30 Stuart, Richard B., and Davis, Barbara. SLIM CHANCE IN A FAT WORLD. unabridged ed. Research Press, 1972. 245 pp. illus. paper $4.75 (book only), $6 (book, wallet, and pen).

Two University of Michigan colleagues—Stuart, a behavioral scientist who is a professor in the School of Medicine, and Davis, a public health nutritionist and lecturer—have produced a step-by-step program of weight reduction through behavioral control of eating, management of food intake, and management of exercise. With modification of behavior the primary theme, little attention is paid to cookery. An easily understood caloric exchange and meal planning system is used. Seven diets are presented, with values ranging from 1200 to 2300 calories. One chapter provides programmed instruction on nutrition. A packet of food exchanges, meal planning, and exercise tally cards accompany the larger book; the same material is bound into the smaller one. The heavily footnoted, unabridged edition probably is too advanced for the average reader, but a simplified version is also available (*see* entry 31).

food value charts & tables	fat: total	recommended dietary allow-
caloric exchanges	protein	ances (RDA)
calories	height/weight charts	references
carbohydrates	meal plans	

*New York City Department of Health, Bureau of Nutrition, *Recommended Nutrition Books for Popular Reading* (1972), p. 10.

31 Stuart, Richard B., and Davis, Barbara. SLIM CHANCE IN A FAT WORLD. condensed ed. Research Press, 1972. 116 pp. illus. paper $3.

This highly abridged version of entry 30 eliminates nearly all of the complex theoretical and background information and certain appendix material, concentrating instead on direct action and results.

food value charts & tables	height/weight charts	recommended dietary allow-
caloric exchanges	meal plans	ances (RDA)

32 Glenn, Morton, B., M.D. HOW TO GET THINNER ONCE AND FOR ALL. Dutton, 1965. 239 pp. index. hard $5.98.

Past president of the American College of Nutrition, the author was associated with the well-known obesity and nutrition clinics of the New York City Department of Health. The reducer's life-style, motivation, and nutritional needs are given primary attention. Detailed selection charts indicate the proper diets and meal plans for men and women of varying ages, heights, and degrees of overweight. The food plan is based on a system of caloric exchanges. Several chapters deal realistically with the temptation to overeat in countless home, business, and social situations. Although the book has more text than the average one of this subject, the author's use of anecdotes makes it both entertaining and informative.

beverages, alcoholic	restricted	meal plans
food lists	guest dining	restaurant dining
permitted	height/weight charts	

33 Netzer, Corinne, with Elaine Chaback. THE BRAND-NAME CALORIE COUNTER. Dell, 1971. 188 pp. index. paper $1.25.

An incredible quantity of information has been assiduously gathered and admiraby organized in one of the largest lists of brand name food values published. (Bowes and Church's work, entry 177, covers 25 additional food values and may approach the number of brand name entries, but the brand names are not always easy to discern.) According to the book's jacket, 5000 listings are included. Every imaginable type of food—from luncheon meat and rice to canned vegetables, frozen pizza, taco seasoning, and malted milk balls—is covered. The cheese and cheese products section alone contains some 300 listings. In explaining how to use the book, the author cautions the reader not to compare caloric values of foods if the portion of one is given in weight and the other in volume. Caloric values for regular, unprocessed foods (lettuce, potatoes, broiled chicken, etc.) are not included nor are values for low-calorie products. The tables are cross-referenced, and the index is very good.

Although the book was hailed as a valid and long overdue contribution by the reviewer in the prestigious *Journal of the American Dietetic Association* (55: 387, 1969), it was placed on the nonrecommended list in *Selected Nutrition References* (1972) published by the Massachusetts Department of Public Health without comment. The latter's negative stance may be due to the author's exuberant and irreverent sense of humor in ridiculing typical diet fare, and her stated preference for a Baby Ruth nugget over half a cantaloupe for dessert, or it may be due to the book's endorsement by Dr. Irwin Stillman, whose own diet books have come under fire from most dietitians and orthodox nutritionists.

beverages, alcoholic	food value charts & tables
brand name information	brand name products
convenience foods	calories

34 Antonetti, Vincent W. THE COMPUTER DIET: A WEIGHT CONTROL GUIDE. Evans, 1973. 282 pp. illus. hard $6.95.

Despite its title, this book is not a bloodless and depersonalized computer print-out, but a readable, fascinating work. The author is a mechanical engineer who specializes in data processing, and much of the book is derived from principles he first published in the *American Journal of Clinical Nutrition*. His article, "The Equations Governing Weight Change," is reprinted in the appendix. Disturbed by claims that a single diet would produce the same weight loss in people of widely varying physiques, he determined to do a mathematical analysis of weight change in human beings. Using existing data and formulas, he ran a digital computer analysis of the number of days required to lose a particular amount of weight based on the age, sex, height, weight, amount of physical activity, and caloric intake of the individual. Nearly half the book is devoted to the resulting charts and tables. Weight maintenance is covered in the same fashion. Numerous diets, with a week's menus, are presented for both men and women at the 900, 1200, 1500, 1800, and 2100 calorie levels (the latter for men only).

beverages, alcoholic	food value charts & tables	meal plans
bibliography	calories	menus: everyday
	height/weight charts	references

35 Bolian, Polly. GROWING UP SLIM. American Heritage Publishing Co., 1971. 150 pp. illus. hard $3.95.

This rather complete book on weight reduction offers a combined program of restricted food intake and body-firming exercises. While packed with charts, lists, questionnaires, and other practical information, the tone of the book comes across as personal without being cloying or cute. The dieting teenager is encouraged to learn good habits of nutrition and exercise and to bear the responsibility for putting them into practice. Nearly one-third of the book is devoted to exercises and personal appearance; illustrations depict both boys and girls. Food charts allow the option of either calorie counting or a system of caloric exchanges. The addition of an index would be helpful.

food value charts & tables	height/weight charts	recipes: 15
caloric exchanges	lunches, packed	calories
calories	meal plans	youth diets
guest dining	menus: everyday	

36 David, Lester. SLIMMING FOR TEEN-AGERS. Pocket Books (Simon & Schuster) in association with *This Week* magazine, 1966. 76 pp. paper $1.

The author of this readable book is a 1964 winner of the Certificate of Capital Recognition in the American Medical Association Medical Journal Awards Competition. The book guides teenagers in evaluating and understanding their overweight problems, and in establishing eating habits based on sensible nutrition. A five-point system for weight reduction, utilizing a simplified system of caloric exchanges or equivalents, is outlined. One chapter contains suggestions from Camp Seascape, a successful weight reducing camp for teenagers; another summarizes and reinforces material through a question-and-answer format.

menus: everyday, holiday	youth diets

Brochures and Product-Related Materials

37 American Dietetic Assn. A NEW WEIGH OF LIFE. 1973. single-page folder. illus. paper $.06; $5.25/100.

Fundamental information about weight loss, utilizing a simple caloric exchange system.

food value charts & tables   height/weight charts
  caloric exchanges   meal plans

38 National Dairy Council. THE FOOD WAY TO WEIGHT REDUCTION. 1961. 13 pp. illus. paper $.15.

Menus and meal plans for 1000, 1200, 1400, and 1800 calorie diets, with abbreviated list of caloric exchanges.

food value charts & tables   guest dining   menus: everyday
  caloric exchanges   height/weight charts   restaurant dining
                                   meal plans

39 National Dairy Council. PERSONALIZED WEIGHT CONTROL. 1966. 15 pp. illus. paper $.14

Practical brochure with everyday advice on weight reduction, stressing use of basic four food groups.

food lists   guest dining   restaurant dining
  restricted   lunches, packed

40 National Dairy Council. WEIGHT CONTROL SOURCE BOOK. 1966. 20 pp. illus. paper $.25.

This is a review of published information on obesity, and includes references to the prevalence and risk of overweight, influences, fads, dietary regimes, and recent research.

glossary   height/weight charts   references

41 National Dairy Council. YOUR CALORIE CATALOG. 1965. 14 pp. illus. paper $.10.

This booklet includes a listing of protein and calorie values for approximately 150 foods and a self-check record for food consumption.

food value charts & tables   protein
  calories   height/weight charts

42 U.S. Dept. of Agriculture. CALORIES AND WEIGHT, THE USDA POCKET GUIDE. Home and Garden Bulletin No. 364. 1970. 75 pp. index illus. paper $1.

Handy booklet outlining sensible weight reduction plans; fairly extensive list of caloric values.

food value charts & tables   height/weight charts
  calories

43 U.S. Dept. of Agriculture. FOOD AND YOUR WEIGHT. Home and Garden Bulletin No. 74. 1973. 37 pp. illus. paper $.40.

A more complete guide to weight reduction (and weight gain) than the pocket-size booklet (entry 42).

food value charts & tables   height/weight charts
  calories   menus: everyday

44 Sunkist Growers. THE CALIFORNIA SLIM THING. 36 pp. illus. paper $.25.

Colorful, attractive cookbook with good selection of recipes utilizing citrus fruits; illustrated exercises.

height/weight charts   recipes: 35
menus: everyday   calories
               servings

45 Kansas Wheat Commission. THE LOVES OF KERNEL BEARD. 1973. 15 pp. illus. paper. free.

Tips on weight reduction and nutrition presented in narrative form; pocket-size daily food guide utilizing modified system of caloric exchanges is included.

food value charts & tables   height/weight charts   recipes: 2
  caloric exchanges   meal plans   seasonings

46 United Fresh Fruit & Vegetable Assn. NUTRITION NOTES: OBESITY HAS MANY ANGLES. 1966 12 pp. paper $.25.

A review, by means of abstracts, of some of the extensive literature on obesity. Four parts are General, Physiological Aspects, Psychologic Considerations, and Treatment by Exercise.

references   youth diets

47 Worthington Foods. LOW CALORIE, LOW CHOLESTEROL RECIPES. 1971. single-page folder. free.

Folder with soup and main dish recipes uses manufacturer's brand name textured vegetable protein (TVP) products.

recipes: 10   diabetic exchanges
  calories

48 American Medical Assn. THE HEALTHY WAY TO WEIGH LESS. 1973. single-page folder. illus. paper $.25.

A simple brochure that gives the basic facts about how many calories are needed to maintain body weight, how fast extra pounds can be lost.

height/weight charts

49 Good Housekeeping. COMPLETE CALORIE GUIDE. Hearst, 1970. 49 pp. paper $.35.

A handy pocket-size calorie counter that includes some 400 entries, this booklet explains the basic four food groups, and reducing and maintenance plans at 1200,

1800, and 2000 calorie levels. There is a good demonstration of how to calculate the number of calories in a recipe.

beverages, alcoholic
food value charts & tables
  calories

height/weight charts
meal plans
references

50 Nutrition Foundation. OBESITY. 1966. 15 pp. paper. single copy free; multiples $.10 prepaid.

General plan for weight reduction with emphasis on avoiding fad diets.

food value charts & tables
  caloric exchanges
height/weight charts

meal plans
restaurant dining

51 Public Affairs Committee. OVERWEIGHT—A PROBLEM FOR MILLIONS. 1973. 24 pp. illus. paper $.35.

A discussion of the dangers of overweight for adults and children, with guidelines for sensible reducing.

bibliography

height/weight charts

youth diets

52 Rice Council of America. RICE: LOW-CALORIE MENUS AND RECIPES. 1970. 28 pp. illus. paper free.

Main dishes, salads, and side dishes utilizing rice; menus are for a 1200 calorie diet.

menus: everyday
recipes: 20

calories
servings

Periodicals

53 WEIGHT WATCHERS® MAGAZINE. 21st Century Communications. 12 issues. $5/yr.

An attractive, popular magazine that developed from the well-known weight reduction program of the same name, this monthly periodical always contains numerous recipes. The recipes, which are planned to fit a caloric exchange system, are conveniently indexed in the back of every issue.

B-2. High Caloric Diets

High caloric diets are a form of nutritional rehabilitation, and most frequently are prescribed for persons recovering from a serious illness or surgery. Calorie, protein, vitamin, and mineral consumption are increased beyond what would be required under normal circumstances. Several books include information on these diets.

For high calorie recipes *see* Protein-restricted diets: 165; Multiple diets: 168, 170.

For supplementary information on high caloric diets *see* Allergy diets: 1; Calorie-restricted diets: 28; Multiple diets: 171, 172; Food composition and values: 177, 178, 179, 180, 181; Nonprofessional nutrition education: 183, 186, 191; Vegetarian diets: 206.

C.
Carbohydrate Modifications

C-1. Galactose-Free Diets

Galactose-free diets eliminate galactose, a natural sugar, or carbohydrate, from the diet. Milk and milk products are avoided, as well as liver, peas, lima beans, beets, and certain other foods. Such diets are prescribed in cases of galactosemia, an inherited disorder that can result in mental retardation, growth failure, and other serious consequences.

For galactose-free recipes *see* Multiple diets: 171.

C-2. Hypoglycemia Diets

Commonly known as low blood sugar, spontaneous hypoglycemia is a disorder in carbohydrate metabolism in which the body produces too much insulin—the opposite of diabetes mellitis. Also called hyperinsulinism, often it is due to poor dietary habits rather than to a physical condition. Diet therapy calls for a reduced intake of carbohydrate in concentrated sweets, an increase in protein, and small, frequent feedings on a regular basis.

For supplementary information on hypoglycemia diets *see* Multiple diets: 171.

Cookbooks

54 Revell, Dorothy Tompkins, R. D. HYPOGLYCEMIA CONTROL COOKERY. Berkley, 1973. 192 pp. index. paper $1.25.

Popularly known as low blood sugar, hypoglycemia has inspired a great many books. This title, however, which was written by a dietitian who has done several other highly respected diet cookbooks, is the only one that has been recommended. In a brief introduction to a well-organized book, the author outlines the principal features of the diet, and provides one week's menus. Extensive lists of foods with their carbohydrate content are given; the brand name information includes soups, canned and frozen entrées, and kosher foods. A practical question-and-answer section discusses artificial sweeteners and emergency foods. The unmistakably American home-style recipe collection encompasses all the easy, everyday favorites, such as cinnamon toast and

23

chili con carne, while including a few surprises, such as pumpkin pie parfait and tomato sherbet.

beverages, alcoholic
brand name information
food value charts & tables
   brand name products

carbohydrates
menus: everyday
recipes: 320
   carbohydrates

servings
references
sweeteners, artificial

D.
Consistency Modifications

D-1. Fiber-Restricted Diets

Fiber-restricted diets, which many lay persons term ulcer or bland diets, call for a minimum of indigestible carbohydrates and tough connective tissue in an otherwise normal diet. Consistency or texture of the food is changed rather than nutrient content. Usually such diets are prescribed for gastric and duodenal ulcers and for gastritis. Fiber-restricted diets have changed considerably over the years, and are much less restrictive than they once were. Nonetheless, many dietitians and physicians feel that their application rests more upon tradition than on clearly established scientific principles.

For supplementary information on fiber-restricted diets *see* Diabetic diets: 114, 115, 119; Multiple diets: 171, 172.

Cookbooks

For additional fiber-restricted recipes *see* Multiple diets: 168, 169, 170.

55 Rubin, Harold. THE ULCER DIET COOK BOOK. Evans, 1963. 223 pp. index. hard $5.95.
Recipe Index: Fiber-restricted.

One of the more complete cookbooks on this subject, this particular work was compiled by an art designer who wanted to add more interest and variety to his bland diet. Although the reviewer in the *Journal of the American Dietetic Association* (43: 474, 1963) takes exception to some of the introductory statements that restrict the dark meat of chicken, American cheese, and salt, she nonetheless highly recommends the book for its recipes. Three practical, and unusual, features are the treatment of shopping advice, blender recipes, and ideas for between-meal snacks for ulcer sufferers. The recipe collection is broad and reasonably varied; individual recipes are marked as appropriate for either a restricted "early phase" or more liberal "later phase" diet. The early and late phase recipes are grouped together in the same chapters, but each is indexed separately in addition to being included in a general index for the whole book. Showing concern for thrift, the cook's time, and the concept of family dining, the author has gathered together in one chapter a number of recipes for the nondieter that use as their basic ingredients foods cooked or partially prepared for the bland diet. The menus, which are divided into the early and later phase diets, are unusual in providing a number of selections for restaurant meals. Another set of menus minimizes special cooking and meal planning by presenting diet and nondiet meals together.

food lists   menus: everyday   servings
  permitted   recipes: 215   restaurant dining
guest dining   diet categories

56 Bruyère, Toni Marsh, and Robey, Sidney Jean. FOR GOURMETS WITH ULCERS. Norton, 1971. 226 pp. index. hard $6.95.
Recipe Index: Fiber-restricted.

The co-authors of this book are both thoroughly experienced in the preparation of French cuisine and are both writers. The result of their collaboration is the most complete and most appealing collection of recipes for this type of diet. Although the recipes are elegant, it would be a mistake to regard this as a book completely devoted to French cooking. The introduction notes that high caloric and cholesterol value of many of the recipes, but points out that all the recipes have been tested with fat-free milk, low-fat cottage cheese, and polyunsaturated substitutes for the richer ingredients. Guidelines and tips for ulcer diet cooking are provided at the beginning of most chapters. One reviewer questions the authors' advice not to use commercial mayonnaise and their statement that rice contains acid-forming elements, but in less quantity than beef or eggs (Patricia M. Kelly, R.D., private communication, June 28, 1974). The selection of recipes is broad, and includes appetizers, sauces, shakes, and other beverages in addition to the usual categories of meat, poultry, fish, and vegetables. The recipes are simple, and make good use of such convenience foods as canned soups and frozen vegetables.

convenience foods
recipes: 270
  servings

Brochures

57 Good Housekeeping. BLAND DIET COOKBOOK. Hearst, 1968. 59 pp. paper $.50.
Recipe Index: Fat-restricted; Fiber-restricted.

This book spans three different but sometimes overlapping types of diets: a bland (or type of fiber-restricted) diet for ulcers; a combination low-fat (fat-restricted) and bland diet for gall bladder conditions and weight control; and a low-residue diet for those with colitis and similar conditions. Permitted and restricted foods are listed for each of the three diets. Because main dish and vegetable preparation pose the greatest problems in achieving variety, the recipe collection emphasizes these types of foods. Recipes for salads, snacks, and desserts are also included. Each recipe is labeled as to the diet or diets for which it is suitable. For the gall bladder diet (fat-restricted), each recipe lists the number of calories and grams of fat per serving. Unfortunately, this title suffers from the same limitations as the others in this Good Housekeeping series: good content poorly presented through the narrative style of recipe, and the complete lack of an index that discourages full application of the information provided. It is a strange contrast to the multiple-diet Good Housekeeping title by Schoenberg (entry 169) that epitomizes outstanding organization.

convenience foods	restricted
food lists	recipes: 125
permitted	diet categories

D–2. Ulcerative Colitis Diet

Ulcerative colitis diets vary, as allergic reactions are sometimes involved, but they essentially are a type of fiber-restricted diet. Dietary treatment stresses nutritional adequacy.

For supplementary information on ulcerative colitis diets *see* Multiple diets: 171.

Cookbooks

For additional ulcerative colitis diet recipes *see* Fiber-restricted diets: 57.

58 Hanson, Map, M.A. DIET MANAGEMENT FOR ULCERATIVE COLITIS: MENUS, RECIPES, AND METHODS OF FOOD PREPARATION FOR ANTI-INFLAMMATORY TREATMENT. Charles C. Thomas, 1971. 66 pp. index. paper $6.50.
Recipe Index: Allergy.

Written by a home economist, this book presents a diet that is not only bland but also free of milk, eggs, and wheat. Background material and menus comprise two-thirds of the book. The introduction describes a two-phase diet for ulcerative colitis. The author shares practical hints for coping with the diet. Detailed menus for 10 days, along with informal recipes and cooking suggestions, are provided for both the very strict Phase I and the more liberal Phase II diets. The modest recipe collection includes main dishes, desserts, cookies and confections and a few salad dressings and meat marinades.

beverages, alcoholic	food lists	menus: everyday
brand name information	permitted	recipes: 45
convenience foods	restricted	servings
entertaining	lunches, packed	restaurant dining
		seasonings

E.
Fat Modifications

E-1. Fat-Controlled Diets

Fat-controlled, or fat-modified, diets call for a high ratio of polyunsaturated to saturated fatty acids and a reduced intake of cholesterol. The total amount of fat in a fat-controlled diet *may* or *may not* be lower than normal. The nature of fat-controlled cookbooks currently in print does not allow for many fine distinctions in this category, so that all cholesterol-restricted (low-cholesterol), high polyunsaturated/low-saturated fatty acid cookbooks have been placed under a single heading, fat-controlled, which comes under the broader, general heading of Fat Modifications.

Readers should note that fat-controlled diets, prescribed to reduce the risk of heart disease or to lower serum cholesterol, are seldom called "low-fat diets" by dietitians. "Low fat" is probably the term most frequently misapplied by the general public when speaking of therapeutic and special diets. True low-fat diets are correctly known as fat-restricted diets, and are a separate classification under the general heading of Fat Modifications (*see* E–3).

Cookbooks

> For additional fat-controlled recipes *see* Calorie-restricted diets: 47; Fat-restricted diets: 85, 86; Multiple diets: 167, 168, 169, 170, 171; Nonprofessional nutrition education: 185.

59 Bond, Clara-Beth Young, R.D.; Dobbin, E. Virginia, R.D.; Gofman, Helen F., M.D.; Jones, Helen C.; and Lyon, Lenore. THE LOW FAT, LOW CHOLES-TEROL DIET. Doubleday, 1971. 512 pp. index. illus. hard $7.95.
Recipe Index: Fat-controlled.

An amazingly thorough and practical cookbook, it is quite understandable that five authors should be credited for producing this exceptional work. First published in 1951, it was revised 20 years later and is now in its third decade. The reviewer for the *Journal of the American Dietetic Association* (59: 498, 1971) states that the diet outlined in the book is not low in total fat as suggested by the title, but low in saturated fat and in cholesterol. Nearly one-quarter of the book is devoted to background information, how-to advice, tips, menus, tables, and charts. In scope and detail it is comparable to a fat-controlled version of Rombauer's classic, *The Joy of Cooking*.

Divided into three sections, the first discusses all aspects of controlled-fat cookery; the second, which is much shorter, emphasizes calorie-restricted and sodium-restricted cookery; the final part contains a general summary on nutrition with special attention to the controlled-fat diet. A substantial introductory chapter tells how to maintain a nutritionally adequate diet in the face of fat control. Two weeks of menus for a low-saturated fat, low-cholesterol diet are given. The chapters on breakfast, packed lunches, and restaurant dining are much fuller than usual, and the restaurant chapter provides a number of suggested menus. The large, well-rounded recipe collection is fundamentally American cookery with a good representation of favorite foreign dishes, such as beef Stroganoff, teriyaki, and tamale pie. Two separate chapters divide the desserts into fat-controlled and calorie-restricted categories. The book contains a large number of recipes for making controlled-fat substitutes for such dairy products as coffee cream, cream cheese, yogurt, and even whole eggs. These in turn are utilized in a large number of dishes. Low-meat and no-meat main dishes containing ample protein are another special feature.

food lists
  permitted
  restricted
food value charts & tables
  calories
  carbohydrates
  cholesterol
  fat: total; monounsatu-
    rated; polyunsaturated;
    saturated

fat exchanges
protein
lunches, packed
meal plans
menus: everyday
recipes: 450
  calories
  carbohydrates
  cholesterol
  fat: polyunsaturated; sat-
    urated

oil, tsp.
protein
servings
recommended dietary allow-
  ances (RDA)
references
restaurant dining
sweeteners, artificial

60 Payne, Alma Smith, M.A., and Callahan, Dorothy. THE FAT AND SODIUM CONTROL COOKBOOK. Little, Brown, 1965. 473 pp. index. hard $5.95. *Recipe Index:* Fat-controlled.

In a very complete book, the authors present a controlled- or modified-fat diet with the option of combining it with a sodium-restricted diet. Although this is not an unusual diet prescription, it is not often found in a single cookbook. Revised several times since it first appeared in 1953, this title is a staple in diet cookery. The excellent supplementary material guides the cook in nearly every facet of preparing tasty, nutritious meals within the limits of the diet. If Bond's book can be compared with *The Joy of Cooking*, the content and format of this book most closely resemble those of *The Fanny Farmer Cookbook*. The presentation is clear, readable, and practical. Controlled-fat diets, both with and without restricted sodium, are discussed, and a variety of menus is offered for different combinations of sodium, fat, and caloric values. To compensate for the loss of salt in cooking, the authors pay special attention to cooking with spirits and herbs. Other subjects given superior treatment include packed lunches, travel, restaurant dining, freezing, and the use of special products such as low-sodium cheese. The range of recipes covers American favorites in each of the typical categories. The appendix contains extensive lists of food values applicable to the diets involved.

beverages, alcoholic
brand name information
canning

convenience foods
entertaining

food lists
  permitted
  restricted

food value charts & tables
  brand name products
  calories
  carbohydrates
  cholesterol
  fat: total; monounsatu-
    rated (oleic); polyun-

saturated (linoleic); saturated
  potassium
freezing
guest dining
lunches, packed
menus: everyday, holiday

recipes: 210
  calories
  fat: total; saturated
  servings
  sodium
references
restaurant dining
seasonings
sweeteners, artificial

61 Eshleman, Ruthe, and Winston, Mary. THE AMERICAN HEART ASSOCIA-
TION COOKBOOK. David McKay, 1973. 412 pp. index. illus. hard $7.95.
Recipe Index: Fat-controlled.

This book is not a diet book, according to the introduction, but a cookbook that
has been planned to carry out in the kitchen the recommendations of the American
Heart Association with regard to the amount and type of fat consumed by Americans.
The book notes that 40 to 45 percent of the average person's caloric intake is fat. The
goal of the association is to reduce fat calories to 30 to 35 percent of total calories. At
the same time, less than 10 percent of the total calories should come from saturated
fatty acids and up to 10 percent should come from polyunsaturated fatty acids to
promote lower cholesterol. Because fat-controlled cookbooks stretch over such a
broadly defined area, and because many cookbooks in this category are so ambiguous
in establishing their limits for fat intake, it seems unfair to exclude this title from this
category. Thus it is being included.

The shopping advice, cooking hints, menus, and other supplementary features are
all geared to a lower and modified- or controlled-fat intake. One chapter is devoted to
vegetarian main dishes; another offers alternative beakfast suggestions. Controlled-
fat substitutes for sour cream, whipped cream, chocolate, and butter are described,
along with information on using them in the cook's own recipes. The extensive recipe
collection contains many popular standards, as well as imaginative new dishes. The
only omissions seem to be sandwiches and packed lunches.

bibliography
convenience foods
food value charts & tables
  calories
  cholesterol

fat: total; monounsatu-
  rated; polyunsaturated;
  saturated
glossary
guest dining

menus: holiday
recipes: 470
  servings
restaurant dining

62 Liebowitz, Daniel, M.D., Brown, W. Jann, M.D., and Olness, Marlene. COOK
TO YOUR HEART'S CONTENT. Menlo Park, Calif.: Pacific Coast Publishers,
1969, 150 pp. index. illus. paper $4.95.
Recipe Index: Fat-controlled.

This attractive, 8½ X 11 inch book has drawn high praise for its recipes and menus.
At the same time, however, the *Journal of the American Dietetic Association* (57: 47,
1970) reviewer points out that it is incorrectly titled low fat, low salt when the accurate
description of the contents is fat-controlled (or fat-modified) and sodium-restricted.
She notes further that some of the general information about the basis for the
recommended diets and the application of dietary principles is inaccurate. Two other

reviewers question the use of specific brand name products such as coffee whiteners and imitation sour cream.* Background information, therefore, should be taken from other sources. On the positive side, two week's menu guides are provided for 1000, 1500, and 2000 calorie controlled-fat diets for both unrestricted sodium and for restricted sodium. A better than average section on herbs and seasonings suggests ways to compensate for the sometimes bland taste of sodium-restricted dishes. Recipes are planned for fat control, and special instructions accompany each one, giving the cook the option of making a sodium-restricted as well as fat-controlled dish. The collection is a good balance between down-home cooking and international specialties, and ranges from appetizers and sauces through meat, beverages, desserts, and even a chapter on picnic foods.

beverages	fat: unsaturated; satu-	recipes: 280
bibliography	rated	calories
brand name information	sodium	sodium
food value charts & tables	guest dining	restaurant dining
brand name products	measurements: metric/	seasonings
calories	household	sweeteners, artificial

63 Zane, Polly. THE JACK SPRAT COOKBOOK. Harper & Row, 1973. 497 pp. index. illus. hard $10.95.
Recipe Index: Fat-controlled.

A most attractive and inviting book, this title is highly recommended by the major reviewers for its imaginative and practical recipes. The sample menus restrict cholesterol to less than 200 milligrams per day; the ratio of polyunsaturated to saturated fatty acids is greater than 3 to 1. The supplementary information features a good chapter on meal planning, another on shopping, and one on adapting the cook's own recipes to a cholesterol-restricted diet. The glossary contains more technical terms than usual. Daniel Steinberg, M.D., a specialist at the University of California at San Diego Medical School, has contributed a substantial "Primer of Diet and Health Disease" in a question-and-answer format. The author apparently has had a prodigal past in which she recklessly used eggs, cream, butter, and cheese. Yet, of the many books reviewed in this category, hers is one of the most unflinching in confronting that great handicap of cholesterol-restricted cookery: the dearth of dairy products. Now reformed, she has imaginatively converted such seemingly hopeless cases as Welsh rarebit, Swiss fondue, quiche Lorraine, and cheesecake. Moreover, she has devised her own egg substitute. The recipe collection is broad enough to include countless basic American dishes, breakfast ideas, and meatless bean and pasta dishes, as well as a good sampling of international foods, particularly Mexican specialties.

food lists	fat: total; monounsatu-	menus: everyday
permitted	rated; polyunsaturated;	recipes: 560
restricted	saturated	servings
food value charts & tables	glossary	restaurant dining
cholesterol	meal plans	seasonings

*Ruth Reznikoff, R.D., San Diego, private communication (May 30, 1974); Bureau of Nutrition, New York City Dept. of Health. *Recommended Nutrition Books for Popular Reading* (1972), p. 12.

64 Cavaiani, Mabel, R.D. THE LOW CHOLESTEROL COOKBOOK. Henry Regnery, 1972. 258 pp. index. hard $7.95.
Recipe Index: Fat-controlled.

The dietitian author, who has written four other cookbooks, has operated her own kitchen on cholesterol-restricted principles for some 20 years. The introductory section of the book explains practical matters on such cooking, using American Heart Association guidelines. The book's recipes and cooking tips are very good. Convenience foods and mixes in general are evaluated as to their suitability in the appropriate chapters on soups, pies, and puddings, and other helpful advice is given. The collection reflects the author's fondness for small-town American home-style cooking and baking. A short selection of foreign dishes includes English muffins, Cornish pastries, and Irish soda bread. Instant dry milk receives special attention as a useful ingredient, and is assigned a chapter of suggestions and recipes. Many recipes throughout the book carry notes on variations or the advisability of doubling the quantity cooked.

The editorial outlook of the book, as seen in the introduction and in remarks made throughout the different food chapters, bears comment. Although it is true that men are more susceptible to heart disease in younger years than are women, the author seems to imply that only men are susceptible. Moreover, she caricatures a rather silly stereotype by stating that their "masculinity" may be threatened by an inability to consume vast quantities of bacon, eggs, and beef. This is further compounded by placing the onus for saving the "male-only" victim completely on the presumably female cook. Far from unique, this "man-strays, woman-saves" theory of total female responsibility for life-and-death nutrition, which denigrates male comprehension and responsibility to that of a small child, is nearly universal in diet cookbooks. With half the population condemned and the other half absolved of all dietary sins (when presumably everybody eats), it is not surprising that so many lament the state of American nutrition.

convenience foods	freezing
food lists	recipes: 305
permitted	servings
restricted	

65 Cutler, Carol. HAUTE CUISINE FOR YOUR HEART'S DELIGHT. Clarkson N. Potter, 1973. 258 pp. index. illus. hard $6.95.
Recipe Index: Fat-controlled.

Many books claim a haute cuisine pedigree, but this is perhaps the only real blue-blood in the fat-controlled category. The author, who writes a food column for the *Washington Post*, studied for 12 years in Paris at the Cordon Bleu and at l'Ecole des Trois Gourmands (the latter run by Julia Child, Simone Beck, and Louisette Bertholle). Introduced to the idea of a controlled-fat diet by her physician brother-in-law, an early exponent of the cholesterol theory, she undertook to reproduce classic French dishes. Given the carefully defined limits of haute cuisine, her feats of transformation are probably greater than Polly Zane's tour de force, which was accomplished within the ever-flexible boundaries of American cookery. Shopping hints and background information are kept to a minimum. The emphasis is on the recipes, which should satisfy the cook who wants to lavish time and care on her food, and who revels in a long list of ingredients. This definitely is not a book for the person looking for the fastest way to put a meal on the table. Most of the recipes are French, with a sprinkling of Italian, Greek, Russian, and other nationalities. Recipe titles are given in the original language with English subtitles. Unfortunately for the homesick, heart-stricken gourmet seeking bifteck Bercy or suprêmes de volaille au champignons, the index uses only the English recipe titles. The cholesterol content of each recipe is rated on a scale of 1 to 4, but there is no explanation of the quantitative basis employed. The ambiguous designations are for no cholesterol, very low, low, and fairly low cholesterol.

brand name information
food lists
  permitted
  restricted
menus: holiday

recipes: 180
  calories
  cholesterol, rating
  servings

66 Heiss, Kay Beauchamp, R.D., and Heiss, C. Gordon. EAT TO YOUR HEART'S CONTENT: THE LOW CHOLESTEROL GOURMET COOKBOOK. Chronicle Books, 1972. 191 pp. index. illus. hard $6.95.
Recipe Index: Fat-controlled.

Fundamentally a gourmet cookbook, this title is the joint effort of a dietitian and her restaurateur husband. Following the latter's heart attack, they adapted their favorite recipes to the requirements of a low-cholesterol diet. The title page states that the book was done with the cooperation of the American Heart Association. The short introduction presents the rationale for the cholesterol-restricted diet along with a few cooking and shopping hints. Unfortunately, there is no indication of cholesterol levels in the text or in the recipes. A good chapter on classic sauces and popular salad dressings leads into an appetizing collection of international recipes. Most of them are complex, such as Beef Wellington and Pheasant Julius Caesar, but there are a number for simple fare such as potato salad and shrimp salad. The usual food types are covered, including sandwiches and breakfast, but breads are excluded. Egg dishes usually are made with egg whites rather than an egg substitute as in the Zane and Bond titles.

recipes: 260
  servings

67 Revell, Dorothy Tompkins, R.D. CHOLESTEROL CONTROL COOKERY. Berkley, 1973.* 174 pp. index. paper $1.25.
Recipe Index: Fat-controlled.

This book, originally printed in 1961 but completely revised for its paperback publication, is indicative of the type of diet cookbooks that may more frequently reach the general public in the coming years. That is, it more sharply defines the goals and means of highly specialized therapeutic diets than does the average diet cookbook. General dietary management is outlined for the five types of hyperlipoproteinemia and printed in summary form. The cholesterol-lowering diet is based on fat control, while the triglyceride-lowering diet combines fat control and carbohydrate control. In the section on cholesterol-lowering diets, Revell explains dietary procedures in detail, and

---

*The Berkley edition mistakenly gives the copyright date as 1961. The author has indicated through a private conversation that the book was completely revised for its paperback publication in 1973 (Dorothy T. Revell, R.D., July 8, 1974).

gives meal patterns, along with an extensive table of cholesterol values in foods. An exchange list is provided in the appendix. A unique title, this is the only book reviewed that covers triglyceride-lowering diets. The book contains a general outline, meal patterns, exchange lists, and lists of foods to be included or excluded from such diets. The recipe collection is planned for both cholesterol and triglyceride lowering, and for a combination of these two requirements. Considering the sophisticated approach to the diets involved, the recipes are surprisingly quick and easy to prepare. Spanning most major food categories from quick breads and soups to main dishes and desserts, they emphasize basic American food. A special group utilizes a brand name powdered whole-egg substitute.

bibliography	food value charts & tables	triglyceride-lowering
brand name information	cholesterol	exchanges
convenience foods	cholesterol-lowering	meal plans
food lists	exchanges	recipes: 240
permitted	fat: total	sweeteners, artificial
restricted		

68 Keys, Margaret, and Keys, Ancel. THE BENEVOLENT BEAN. Farrar Straus & Giroux, 1972. 192 pp. index. paper $2.45

Both authors are closely associated with the investigation and explanation of the role of cholesterol in diet and disease. Although this book provides recipes for the fat-controlled diet and one chapter describes the authors' cholesterol research that led to their interest in beans, this work is not a guide to the fat-controlled diet. Rather, the focus is on the understanding and enjoyment of peas, lentils, peanuts, chick-peas, soybeans, green beans, and a large variety of dried beans. Approximately one-third of the book comprises a delightfully fascinating account of the bean in history, which would hold the interest of anyone intrigued by food lore. All the recipes, of course, contain beans, and include soups, bean pots, cassoulets (bean stews in the grand manner), main courses, vegetable courses, salads, and soybean dishes. The final chapter focuses on bean cookery in Imperial Rome, and contains modern versions of recipes recorded by Apicius in the first century A.D.

convenience foods	fat: total; polyunsatu-
recipes: 190	rated; saturated
calories	protein
	references

69 Havenstein, Nathalie, and Richardson, Elizabeth. THE ANTI-CORONARY COOKBOOK. Grosset & Dunlap, 1971. 128 pp. index. paper $1.45.
Recipe Index: Fat-controlled.

Both authors are dietitians. Originally published in Australia, this book was complied with the assistance of the National Heart Foundation of Australia. It has since been adapted for American use, and, in general, conforms with the suggestions of the American Heart Association. Divided into two sections, the first and larger part covers the fat-controlled diet. The second part, comprising the final third of the book, is devoted to a calorie-restricted diet. The succinct but pertinent introductory material in each section includes dietary guidelines, cooking and shopping hints, and a week's menus. Each fat-controlled recipe lists the amount of oil (in teaspoons) per serving. A little bit of everything is covered in the recipe collection, the theme of which is simple but tasty food.

food lists
 permitted
 restricted
food value charts & tables
 caloric exchanges

guest dining
height/weight charts
meal plans
menus: everyday

recipes: 175
 servings
restaurant dining

70 Reznikoff, Ruth, R.D. HEART LINE RECIPES. San Diego County Heart Assn., 1973. 58 pp. illus. paper $1 donation.
Recipe Index: Fat-controlled.

The author, who is consulting dietitian for the San Diego County Heart Association, also writes "The Heart Line," a nationally syndicated newspaper column on modified- or controlled-fat cookery. This book is designed to be used with the American Heart Association's leaflet, "The Way to a Man's Heart" (entry 79). The introduction quickly recaps an eight-point guide to low-cholesterol, low-saturated fat shopping and cooking. The genuinely appetizing recipe collection, which includes many selections that have appeared in the Heart Line column, includes simple, everyday dishes as well as many that definitely are in the gourmet class. Unpretentious, this book is a fine example of the high quality in content and format that can be achieved in a publication by even a small publisher.

recipes: 130
 servings

71 Weiss, Elizabeth S., and Wolfson, Rita Parsont. THE GOURMET'S LOW CHOLESTEROL COOKBOOK. Chicago: Henry Regnery, 1973. 165 pp. index. hard $6.95.
Recipe Index: Fat-controlled.

The co-authors are both graduates of the Cordon Bleu Cooking School. Following an explanation of the underlying principles of the controlled-fat diet, the book features a planning guide for the low-cholesterol kitchen. Each chapter of recipes for vegetables, meats, salads, etc., has a list of do's and don'ts and helpful hints for shopping and cooking according to the recommended guidelines. The sensible approach of Ms. Wolfson, who has also written *The Penny-Pincher's Cookbook* and *The One-Pot Cookbook*, is reflected in this volume. Whereas the author's training might lead one to expect only elaborate and complicated recipes, there are many short, easy ones; those requiring a large number of ingredients are not overly time consuming. These are recipes for the average, interested cook. Devotees of true haute cuisine will be more satisfied with Cutler's work (entry 65). Along with many fat-controlled versions of international and American favorites, the authors present a large number of original and intriguing dishes, such as walnut fish, cherry flank steak, sesame burgers, and juniper sauerkraut. Most major food categories are included in the recipe collection, with the exception of breads, sandwiches, beverages, and breakfasts.

food lists
 permitted
 restricted

food value charts & tables
 cholesterol
 fat: total; monounsatu-
  rated (oleic); polyun-
  saturated (linoleic); saturated

recipes: 160
 servings

72 Bennett, Iva, and Simon, Martha. THE PRUDENT DIET. David White, 1973. 324 pp. index. illus. hard $7.95; Bantam. 337 pp. paper $1.95.

Both authors are public health nutritionists in the Bureau of Nutrition, Department of Health, New York City. Working with the late Dr. Norman Jolliffe, they helped develop the controlled- or modified-fat "prudent diet" through the bureau's well-known Anti-Coronary Club. This book explains and implements the prudent diet. Introductory material summarizes the relationship between diet and coronary heart disease, and reviews the history of the Anti-Coronary Club. Practical applications of a controlled-fat diet, weight reduction, the basics of sound nutrition, imaginative meal planning, and menus are also covered. Controlled-fat variations of margarine, yogurt, and sour cream are provided in a chapter on cooking hints, along with suggestions on equipment and ingredient substitutions. Reflecting the diverse ethnic population of New York, the recipes encompass a good many Jewish, German, and Italian selections, along with other international favorites and American standbys. The recipes are not overly complicated. One reviewer sounds a cautionary note on the cholesterol content of recipes containing liver, shrimp, caviar, and whole eggs (Ruth Reznikoff, R.D., private communication, May 30, 1974). The book features a detailed chart on baking and broiling dozens of types of fish.

bibliography	lunches, packed	recipes: 380
glossary	menus: everyday, holiday	servings
height/weight charts		restaurant dining

73 Rosenthal, Sylvia. LIVE HIGH ON LOW FAT. Lippincott, 1968. 328 pp. index. hard $5.95.

This is another book with a misleading title: the diet and recipes are not for a low-fat diet, but for a controlled- or modified-fat diet (*Journal of the American Heart Assn.*, 43: 129, 1963). Following the "prudent diet" originated by the late Dr. Norman Jolliffe of the Bureau of Nutrition, New York City, the author explains the role of cholesterol and what she calls "the friendly fats" (polyunsaturated fatty acids) and then recaps the prudent diet in a separate chapter. Facing the egg problem, she recommends powdered egg whites, providing information on a retail mail-order source. Other suggestions are given for substitute or modified dairy products. The recipe collection combines old favorites and staples of the American table with new or foreign dishes, spanning the spectrum of cookery from soups, vegetables, and salads through casseroles, meats, desserts, and even a brief treatment of breakfast. Many recipes are annotated with interesting serving suggestions. As with several other authors of controlled-fat cookbooks, Ms. Rosenthal apparently could not resist the temptation to share her recipes for such high-cholesterol foods as kidney pie and chopped chicken liver (with eggs!).

brand name information	cholesterol	menus: holiday
convenience foods	fat: monounsaturated;	recipes: 380
food lists	polyunsaturated; satu-	servings
permitted	rated	references
restricted	glossary	restaurant dining
food value charts & tables	guest dining	seasonings
calories	height/weight charts	

Supplementary Books

For additional supplementary information of fat-controlled diets *see* Calorie-restricted diets: 13, 14; Diabetic diets: 113, 114, 117; Multiple diets: 171, 172; Food composition and values: 177, 178, 179, 181; Nonprofessional nutrition education: 198; Vegetarian diets: 206, 207, 210.

74 Weiss, Elizabeth, S., and Wolfson, Rita Parsont. CHOLESTEROL COUNTER. Pyramid, 1973. 61 pp. paper $1.

More than a simple list of food values, this book contains a lot of practical information about shopping, cooking, and meal planning for reducing serum cholesterol. The recipes are taken from the authors' *The Gourmet's Low Cholesterol Cookbook* (entry 71).

food lists	fat: monounsaturated	menus: everyday
permitted	(oleic); polyunsatu-	recipes: 10
restricted	rated (linoleic); satu-	servings
food value charts & tables	rated	
cholesterol		

Brochures and Product-Related Materials

Most of the following American Heart Association booklets are available from your local Heart Association without a doctor's prescription. Some originate in New York, while others, such as those dealing with brand name product lists (entry 75) are published by local chapters and then reprinted by other chapters. The New York headquarters can supply most titles if they are not available locally.

75 American Heart Assn. AVAILABLE PRODUCTS FOR THE CONTROLLED FAT DIET. Chicago and San Francisco. 1972. 21 pp. paper. free locally.

This comprehensive booklet lists a great variety of brand name products that are suitable for controlled-fat diets, including TV dinners, soups, mixes, cookies, and dairy products.

brand name information	food value charts & tables
convenience foods	brand name products
	fat exchanges

76 American Heart Assn. EAT WELL BUT WISELY TO REDUCE YOUR RISK OF HEART ATTACK. 1969. single-page. paper. free. Also available in Spanish (entry 82).

An elementary guide that outlines the ABCs of changing dietary habits to reduce the risk of heart attack.

77 Alameda County Heart Assn. FEWER CALORIES FOR BETTER HEALTH. single-page folder. illus. free locally or $.25. Also available in Spanish (entry 83).

A brochure designed for the Mexican-American that shows how to implement a controlled-fat or calorie-restricted diet.

food lists	menus: everyday
permitted	recipes: 5
restricted	

78 American Heart Assn. RECIPES FOR FAT-CONTROLLED, LOW CHOLES-
TEROL MEALS. 1973. 28 pp. illus. paper. free.

Quite a good collection of recipes for meats, fish, vegetables, desserts, plus cooking tips and advice for adjusting the cook's own recipes to a controlled-fat program.

recipes: 45
  servings

79 American Heart Assn. THE WAY TO A MAN'S HEART. 1972. single-page
folder. illus. paper. free.

Basic facts about controlled-fat diets are presented in a folder that opens into an
attractive wall chart showing recommended foods and those that should be avoided
or used sparingly.

food lists
  permitted
  restricted

80 North Dakota Heart Assn. COOKING TO YOUR HEART'S CONTENT. 49
pp. paper $1.75.
Recipe Index: Fat-controlled.

This booklet is a little difficult to thumb through, but opens nicely on a kitchen
table. Besides many of the standard controlled-fat recipes, it contains some unusual
ones for venison, inexpensive fruit cake, and homemade low-fat cheese.

convenience foods
menus: holiday
recipes: 140

81 Fleischmann's. COOKING WITH EGG BEATERS ™ . Fleischmann's, 1972.
31 pp. illus. paper. free.
Recipe Index: Fat-controlled.

This attractive booklet has a good group of recipes for dishes normally requiring
eggs, including omelets, French toast, and pumpkin pie made with the manufacturer's
cholesterol-free egg substitute.

brand name information   recipes: 35
food lists   servings
  permitted
  restricted

Foreign Language Materials

82 Los Angeles County Heart Assn. COMA BIEN PERO COMA CON PRUDEN-
CIA PARA REDUCIR EL RIESGO DE UN ATAQUE CARDÍACO (Eat Well
but Wisely to Reduce Your Risk of Heart Attack). 1973. single-page folder. free
locally.

This leaflet is a translation of entry 76, and outlines the most important dietary
modifications necessary to reduce the risk of heart attack.

83 Alameda County Heart Assn. MENOS CALORÍAS PARA MEJOR SALUD (Fewer Calories for Better Health) single-page folder. free locally or $.25.

This brochure, a translation of entry 77, designed for the Mexican-American, shows how to implement a controlled-fat or calorie-restricted diet.

food lists
  permitted
  restricted

menus: everyday
recipes: 5

E-2. Fat-Controlled and Sodium-Restricted Diets

Physicians often prescribe a diet that entails both fat control and sodium restriction for cases of congestive heart failure. Many books cover these diets separately (*see* Fat-controlled Diets, E-1; Sodium-restricted Diets, F-2), but only a few deal with them as a combination.

For fat-controlled and sodium-restricted recipes *see* Fat controlled diets: 60, 62.

For supplementary information on fat-controlled and sodium-restricted diets *see* Fat-controlled diets: 59; Fat-restricted diets: 85; Diabetic diets: 114; Food composition and values: 177, 178, 179, 181.

E-3. Fat-Restricted Diets

Fat-restricted diets are true low-fat diets in which the total intake of fatty foods is reduced or restricted, *without* regard to whether the fats are saturated or unsaturated. Such diets typically are prescribed for gall bladder diseases, and are different from fat-controlled diets associated with heart disease and the lowering of serum cholesterol. Because fat-restricted and fat-controlled diets so often are confused by lay persons, the reader should ascertain the *purpose* of the diet lest she or he inadvertently search out information for the wrong diet.

For supplementary information on fat-restricted diets *see* Multiple diets: 171, 172; Food composition and values: 177, 178, 179, 180, 181.

Cookbooks

For additional fat-restricted recipes *see* Fiber-restricted diets: 57; Multiple diets: 168.

84 Stead, Evelyn S., and Warren, Gloria K. LOW-FAT COOKERY. McGraw-Hill, 1959. 284 pp. index. illus. hard $6.95; Arco. $1.45.
Recipe Index: Fat-restricted.

This title by far is the most comprehensive in dealing with the fat-restricted diet. The authors' goal is to provide a guide for limiting fat intake to either 25 grams or 50 grams per day; a week's menu is given for each program. Perhaps because it was first published in 1956 and revised only once in 1959, the book contains a chapter that suggests the use of the low-fat diet as a means of preventing heart disease. The current recommendations of the American Heart Association and of most authorities on modifying the ratio of polyunsaturated to saturated fatty acids are neither mentioned nor exemplified in the recipes. This book, therefore, is not for a fat-modified or fat-controlled diet but for a fat-restricted diet.

An interesting feature is a side-by-side comparison of an original recipe for lasagna and a low-fat version of the same dish, which is used to illustrate the steps that were taken to convert ordinary recipes to fat-restricted ones. The recipes list not only the total fat content and usually the fat per serving but also the fat content of each ingredient containing an appreciable quantity of fat. Many brand name products, especially mixes and cheeses, are used in the recipes. Essentially a collection of American favorites, the recipes span most of the standard food classifications. Particularly good chapters include breakfast, sandwiches, sauces and relishes, and cheese spreads. Extensive charts in the appendix detail the fat content of hundreds of foods, also by brand name. A short chapter covers the sodium-restricted diet.

brand name information	food value charts & tables	recipes: 300
convenience foods	brand name products	fat: total
food lists	fat: total	servings
permitted	menus: everyday	references
restricted		seasonings

85 Brown, Helen B., Ph.D. LOW FAT AND VEGETABLE OIL RECIPES. Cleveland Clinic. 77 pp. $2.80 postpaid.
Recipe Index: Fat-restricted.

Distinctly divided into two sections, this cookbook includes recipes for a fat-restricted diet and others for a fat-controlled diet. Each section contains an equal number of recipes (75), and each has its own table of contents. Section I, the fat-restricted diet, summarizes a few tips on low-fat cookery as an introduction to the recipes, which cover soups, meats, sauces, salads and salad dressings, vegetables, and desserts. Section II, limited to fat-controlled recipes, has only two pages of cooking instructions and a list of equivalents for adapting recipes for use with polyunsaturated vegetable oils. As with the first recipe collection, this one offers a few dishes in each general food category. Two offbeat but intriguing mini-collections describe cottage cheese sandwich fillings and nut confections. As the author notes, the book is not a complete cookbook because the recipes are limited and supplementary information minimal. Rather, it is an attempt to share many of the recipes that were compiled for patients in a dietary research program at the Cleveland Clinic.

food lists	recipes: 150
permitted	servings
restricted	

Brochures

86 Good Housekeeping. 125 FAVORITE LOW-FAT, LOW-CHOLESTEROL RECIPES. Hearst, 1968. 63 pp. paper $.50.
Recipe Index: Fat-restricted.

This booklet contains 100 recipes that are low in total fat and cholesterol, many of which are also low in calories. The final 25 recipes are cholesterol-free, low in saturated fats, and high in polyunsaturated fats (fat-controlled). The introduction notes that the second group of recipes may not be appropriate for a fat-restricted or low-fat diet. A helpful question-and-answer section at the beginning of the book

88 Signore, Juliette M., R.D. KETOGENIC DIET CONTAINING MEDIUM-CHAIN TRIGLYCERIDES. American Dietetic Assn., 1973. 6 pp. paper $.45.

This reprint from the *Journal of the American Dietetic Association* describes a diet used in the control of epileptic seizures among children, which includes recipes for a medium-chain triglyceride meat casserole and pizza.

brand name information	recipes: 2	references
meal plans	carbohydrates	youth diets
menus: everyday	fat: medium-chain triglyc-	
	erides	
	protein	

E–6. Medium-Chain Triglyceride Diets

Medium-chain triglycerides, a special type of fatty acid, have been used since 1964 in the treatment of malabsorption syndromes, such as pancreatitis, tropical and non-tropical sprue, massive resection of the small intestine, cystic fibrosis, and gastrectomy. (Malabsorption syndromes are marked by an inability of the small intestine to absorb nutrients properly and completely.) A commercially prepared formula of MCT® oil is used in food preparation as the primary source of fat in the diet. Long-chain triglycerides (LCT), which occur naturally in meat, fish, poultry, milk, and oils, usually are restricted.

For medium-chain triglyceride diet recipes *see* Multiple diets: 167.

Brochures

89 Bowman, Ferne, Ph.D., R.D. MCT COOKIES, CAKES, AND QUICK BREADS: QUALITY AND ACCEPTABILITY. American Dietetic Assn., 1973. 6 pp. illus. paper $.55.

This reprint from the *Journal of the American Dietetic Association* gives recipes for cookies, muffins, raisin bread, date bread, and banana bread, utilizing MCT oil. Modifications for high-altitude baking are noted.

brand name information	fat: fatty acids, essential;	protein
recipes: 5	long-chain triglyc-	servings
calcium	erides; medium-chain	vitamins
calories	triglycerides	references
carbohydrates	iron	

90 Howard, Barbara D., R.D.; and Morse, Ellen H., Ph.D., R.D. MUFFINS AND PASTRY MADE WITH MEDIUM-CHAIN TRIGLYCERIDE OIL. American Dietetic Assn., 1973. 2 pp. illus. paper $.30.

This reprint from the *Journal of the American Dietetic Association* presents recipes that use MCT oil.

brand name information	references
recipes: 2	
servings	

E–7. Triglyceride-Lowering Diets

These diets are part of the more complex scheme of diet therapy that is emerging called hyperlipoproteinemia diets. Triglycerides are the major component in fat covers the ground rules for controlled- or modified-fat diets, and lists suggestions for cooking, packing lunches, and dining in restaurants. The principal recipe group, for low fat and low cholesterol, includes soups, main dishes and casseroles, vegetables, salads, and desserts. Nearly all of the second group of recipes, for controlled-fat requirements, is devoted to baked goods with a few for salad dressings. As with the other Good Housekeeping booklets in this series, excellent information is buried in a dreadful format, and will benefit only those cooks patient enough to read narrative style recipes and to relocate favorites without an index.

convenience foods	recipes: 125	fat: total
lunches, packed	calories	restaurant dining
	cholesterol	

E-4. Hyperlipoproteinemia Diets

Hyperlipoproteinemia is a term used to indicate elevated levels of lipids, or fatlike substances, in the blood. There are five types of hyperlipoproteinemia, each with different causes and effects. Diet therapy may involve not only modified fat intake but variations in carbohydrate intake as well. New even to some dietitians, and virtually unknown to the general public, hyperlipoproteinemia diets actually encompass some well-known fat-controlled diets designed to lower serum cholesterol. Greater understanding has resulted in the careful sorting out and labeling of diets that are still lumped together under the tags "fat-controlled" or "low-cholesterol." No doubt new books will appear on this subject, but since this area of diet therapy is so complex, the reader is cautioned to rely on only the most authoritative sources.

For hyperlipoproteinemia diet recipes *see* Fat-controlled diets: 67.

For supplementary information on hyperlipoproteinemia diets *see* Multiple diets: 171.

E-5. Ketogenic Diets

Although diet therapy for epilepsy has largely been superseded by the use of medication, it is still employed in some cases. Ketogenic diets are extremely low in carbohydrate, moderately high in protein, and very high in fat.

For supplementary information on ketogenic diets *see* Multiple diets: 171.

Brochures

87 Lasser, Joyce L., and Brush, Miriam K., Ph.D., R.D. AN IMPROVED KETOGENIC DIET FOR TREATMENT OF EPILEPSY. American Dietetic Assn., 1973. 5 pp paper $.45.

The development of a list of food equivalents, or exchange lists, for ketogenic diets is described in this reprint from the *Journal of the American Dietetic Association*. The lists are presented, along with menus and meal plans for implementation.

brand name information	fat exchanges	menus: everyday
food value charts & tables	ketogenic exchanges	references
brand name products	meal plans	youth diets

When triglyceride levels in the blood are above normal and cholesterol is in the desired range, a triglyceride-lowering diet may be prescribed. They may also be used when both cholesterol and triglyceride levels are high. Instead of focusing only on dietary fat, by implementing a higher ratio of polyunsaturated to saturated fats, triglyceride-lowering diets also restrict the use of concentrated carbohydrates, especially those found in sweets.

For triglyceride-lowering recipes *see* Fat-controlled diets: 67.

For supplementary information on triglyceride-lowering diets *see* Multiple diets: 171.

F.
Mineral Modifications

F-1. Copper-Restricted Diets

Copper-restricted diets are used for Wilson's disease, a rare, inherited disorder in which the body absorbs and stores large amounts of copper, causing a variety of symptoms. Diet therapy calls for a reduction in copper-rich foods.

For supplementary information on copper-restricted diets *see* Multiple diets: 171.

ures

vler, Marilyn R., and Jelenc, Margaret A. RECIPES FOR LOW-COPPER TS. American Dietetic Assn., 1970. 3 pp. paper $.30.

copper diets, which are used in the treatment of Wilson's disease, frequently are low in calories and limited in variety. Ten recipes for baked desserts, including cookies, pies, and cobblers, are the focus of this reprint from the *Journal of the American Dietetic Association*.

recipes: 10	copper	protein
calcium	fat: total	servings
calories	iron	vitamins

F-2. Sodium-Restricted Diets

Sodium-restricted diets, often called low-salt diets, restrict not only the use of table salt (sodium chloride) but also the intake of foods naturally rich in sodium and those that have accumulated appreciable quantities of sodium through food processing techniques. Such diets usually are prescribed in cases of edema (abnormal accumulation of body fluids) associated with congestive heart failure, toxemia of pregnancy, and certain kidney diseases. They also are used in some cases of hypertension, or high blood pressure.

For supplementary information on sodium-restricted diets *see* Calorie-restricted diets: 13; Fat-controlled diets: 59; Fat-restricted diets: 84, 85; Diabetic diets: 114, 115; Multiple diets: 171, 172; Food composition and values: 177, 178, 179, 180, 181; Vegetarian diets: 207.

Cookbooks

For additional sodium-restricted recipes *see* Fat-controlled diets: 60, 62; Multiple diets: 167, 168, 169, 170.

92 Bagg, Elma W. COOKING WITHOUT A GRAIN OF SALT. Doubleday, 1964. 224 pp. index. hard $5.95; Bantam. paper $1.65.
Recipe Index: Sodium-restricted.

This book is planned for a diet of 500 milligrams of sodium per day, and offers the option of calorie control since the number of calories is given for each recipe. Charts and how-to information take up a full one-third of the book. The author points out unsuspected sources of sodium in toothpaste, medications, food additives, and convenience foods. One chart lists the sodium content of drinking water in more than 100 U.S. cities, and another compares sodium values for ordinary foods and their special, sodium-restricted counterparts. For those traveling abroad, the author tells how to say "no salt" in 13 foreign languages. Although restaurant dining is discussed, a reviewer for the Missouri Dietetic Association (Suppl. No. 2: 7, 1970) comments that the recommendations "seem unnecessarily restricted." Comprising an all-round collection of American food favorites, the recipes have been adapted to meet both taste and sodium-restriction requirements by emphasizing the use of herbs and spirits. In addition to a good selection of soups, salads, sandwiches, sauces, meat, seafood (with a long list of seasonally available fish), vegetables, and desserts, special attention is given to breakfast, holiday, and party foods.

bibliography	food value charts & tables	recipes: 235
convenience foods	calories	calories
food lists	sodium	servings
permitted	guest dining	sodium
restricted	lunches, packed	restaurant dining
		seasonings

93 Johnston, Barbara, and Koh, Maria, R.D. HALT! NO SALT: A CONTROLLED SODIUM COOKBOOK. Dietary Research, 1972. 64 pp. illus. paper $2.20 postpaid.
Recipe Index: Sodium-restricted.

The collaborators on this book are the mother of a kidney patient and donor for her teenage daughter's kidney transplant, and a clinic dietitian at the University of Washington Hospital in Seattle. The young patient, Linda Johnston, contributed the snappy title and cover design. In the supplementary material a number of interesting situations are discussed, for example, how to get salt-free potato chips and corn chips, and some honest revelations about the deficiencies of most sodium-restricted baked goods. A short list of substitutions offers variations on sodium-restricted ingredients. Unlike most other sodium-restricted cookbooks, this one does not employ spirits for flavoring. Also, it has a much lighter hand with the herbs. The recipes are far less sophisticated than the average sodium-restricted collection, no doubt because they were developed for a teenager rather than for an older person. From that standpoint it fills a real need for simple home cooking and easy lunches. The lack of an index is regrettable since there are so many good items: dill pickles, bread and butter pickles, tacos, pizza, and eight different kinds of peanut butter sandwiches. An entire chapter is devoted to sandwiches. Other categories covered are appetizers, beverages, soups and sauces, meat, vegetables, dressings, baked goods, and desserts.

brand name information	calories	recipes: 120
convenience foods	potassium	calories
food lists	sodium	protein
permitted	guest dining	servings
restricted	lunches, packed	sodium
food value charts & tables	measurements: metric/	restaurant dining
brand name information	household	seasonings

Brochures and Product-Related Materials

94 Fleischmann's. LOW-SODIUM DIETS CAN BE DELICIOUS. 1966. 38 pp. illus. paper. free.
Recipe Index: Sodium-restricted.

This handy booklet combines several good features for a 1000 milligram per day sodium-restricted diet. Following some general rules, the book presents a list of sodium exchanges, or groups of common foods arranged in categories according to their similar sodium content. (This is yet another application of the exchange system originally conceived for diabetic diets.) The exchanges are then utilized in 10 day's meal plans and menus. The final section contains an abbreviated recipe selection for main dishes, breads, vegetables, salad dressings, and desserts.

brand name information	food value charts & tables	meal plans
food lists	brand name products	menus: everyday
permitted	calories	recipes: 35
restricted	sodium	servings
	sodium exchanges	sodium

95 Good Housekeeping. IF YOUR DOCTOR PRESCRIBES A LOW SODIUM DIET. Hearst, 1963. 31 pp. paper $.50.
Recipe Index: Sodium-restricted.

The contents of this book are very similar to those of the Fleischmann title cited earlier (entry 94). The format is much superior to the other titles in the Good House-keeping diet booklet series. Sodium exchanges are given (although they do not dove-tail with the previous title), and are used in the recipes. Meal plans and menus are provided for 500, 1000, and 1500 milligram diets for three different caloric levels: 1200, 1500, and 2000 calories. Recipes are limited to baked goods, puddings and desserts, and salad dressings.

food value charts & tables	meal plans	recipes: 25
sodium	menus: everyday	servings
sodium exchanges		sodium exchanges

96 San Francisco Heart Assn. LOW SODIUM RECIPES. 1969. 11 pp. paper $.25.
Recipe Index: Sodium-restricted.

This booklet is devoted entirely to recipes, with no supplementary information provided.

lunches, packed	servings
recipes: 25	sodium
calories	

97 San Francisco Heart Assn. YOUR LOW SODIUM DIET. 1973. 30 pp. illus. paper $.50.
Recipe Index: Sodium-restricted.

A substantial amount of brand name information is given in this booklet, along with good recipes, cooking tips, and hints on dining out. Recipes are given for home-made biscuit mix and for cottage cheese.

brand name information	guest dining	restaurant dining
food value charts & tables	recipes: 50	seasonings
calories	calories	
sodium	servings	
	sodium	

The following Heart Association booklets may be available from your local chapter of the American Heart Association. You can find your nearest chapter by contacting the New York office.

98 Alameda County Heart Assn. COOKING WITHOUT SALT. single-page folder. illus. paper. free locally or $.25. Also available in Spanish (entry 102).

Simple recipes and menu suggestions are made for a Mexican-American sodium-restricted diet.

food lists	menus: everyday
permitted	recipes: 5
restricted	

99 Los Angeles County Heart Assn. SPECIAL FOODS AND FOOD PRODUCTS FOR USE WITH SODIUM OR SALT RESTRICTED DIETS. 1973. 13 pp. paper. free locally.

Dozens of brand name sodium-restricted products are listed in this pamphlet, along with the names of stores in the Los Angeles area where they can be bought. Similar booklets are often published by other Heart Associations.

brand name information	convenience foods

100 Campbell Soup Co. COOKING WITH LOW SODIUM SOUPS. single-page folder. illus. paper. free.
Recipe Index: Sodium-restricted.

The manufacturer's products are put to good use in tempting casseroles, soups, sauces, and an aspic. The leaflet is accompanied by a flyer giving a detailed food analysis of the products.

brand name information	carbohydrates	recipes: 12
convenience foods	fat: total	calories
food value charts & tables	potassium	servings
calories	protein	sodium
	sodium	

101 Coleman, Patricia Hepworth, M.S., and McLaren, Barbara A., Ph.D. A MATTER OF TASTE. Univ. of Toronto, 1970. 36 pp. paper $2.50 postpaid. Also available in French (entry 103).
Recipe Index: Sodium-restricted.

A basic guide to a sodium-restricted diet of 400 milligrams, this booklet emphasizes meal planning and everyday-type recipes. A supplement gives convenient recipes for cookie mix and a muffin mix, with many suggestions for variations.

convenience foods	meal plans	recipes: 40
food lists	menus: everyday	servings
permitted		seasonings
restricted		

Foreign Language Materials

102 Alameda County Heart Assn. COCINANDO SIN SAL. single-page folder. illus. paper. free locally or $.25. Also available in English (entry 98).

Simple recipes and menu suggestions are made for a Mexican-American sodium-restricted diet.

food lists	menus: everyday
permitted	recipes: 5
restricted	

103 Coleman, Patricia Hepworth, M.S., and McLaren, Barbara A., Ph.D. UNE QUESTION DE GOÛT (A Matter of Taste). Univ. of Toronto, 1970. 32 pp. illus. $2.50 postpaid. Also available in English (entry 101).

A basic guide to a sodium-restricted diet of 400 milligrams, this booklet emphasizes meal planning and everyday-type recipes. There is no supplement as in the English edition (entry 101).

food lists	meal plans	recipes: 25
permitted	menus: everyday	servings
restricted		seasonings

G.
Protein-Fat-Carbohydrate Modifications

G-1. Diabetic Diets

Diabetes mellitis is a disorder that affects metabolism, especially that of carbohydrates. Although medication plays an important role in some cases, the regulation of diet is vital for all diabetics. Diabetic diets essentially are normal diets, a fact that surprises many persons. The proper balance of protein, fat, and especially carbohydrates is maintained. Particular attention is given to measured quantities of food taken at regular intervals so that the body's inadequate capacity for metabolizing carbohydrates will not be overloaded.

Diabetics must know the composition of foods so that they can control nutrient intake. As is explained in the section entitled "How to Use This Book," food composition and measurement are approached in two ways: by counting each calorie and every gram of carbohydrate, fat, and protein or by using the simpler diabetic exchange lists. Many diabetic cookbooks use both systems; some use only one.

For cookbooks using diabetic exchange system for recipes *see* 12, 24, 47, 104, 105, 106, 107, 108, 109, 110, 111, 112, 113, 116, 118, 120, 129, 130, 131, 136, 144, 167, 169, 170, 171.

For cookbooks using grams of carbohydrates, fat, and protein for recipes *see* 24, 104, 106, 107, 112, 113, 127, 144, 170.

Cookbooks

For additional diabetic recipes *see* Calorie-restricted diets: 12, 24, 47; Multiple diets: 167, 168, 169, 170, 171.

104 Behrman, Deaconess Maude, and Levinson, Leonard L., ed. A COOKBOOK FOR DIABETICS. American Diabetes Assn., 1969. 172 pp. index. spiral/paper $1.
Recipe Index: Diabetic.

This cookbook is the one most frequently recommended by dietitians for diabetics, and is an official publication of the American Diabetes Association. The majority of recipes and menus were developed by Deaconess Maude Behrman, who for 12 years was the consulting dietitian to the ADA *Forecast* magazine, a bimonthly publication for diabetics and their families. Recipes in this useful and comprehensive compendium of information on diabetic cooking and eating are mainly American favorites, and are calculated for both the diabetic exchange and gram weight systems. The yield of most recipes, however, is usually for only one serving or portion. Proper use of artificial sweeteners and seasonings are covered in brief chapters, with fuller treatment given to the purpose and calculation of caloric measurements. Menus and recipes for special occasion eating include traditional foods for Passover, Christmas, cookouts, Easter, Lenten fasting, picnics, and Thanksgiving. The sturdy metal binding allows the book to lie flat while in use.

canning	freezing	carbohydrates
convenience foods	lunches, packed	diabetic exchanges
food value charts & tables	meal plans	fat: total
calories	menus: everyday, holiday	protein
carbohydrates	recipes: 245	servings
diabetic exchanges	calories	seasonings
fat: total		sweeteners, artificial
protein		

105 Donahoe, Virginia M. THE NEW DIABETIC COOKING MADE EASY. Diabetes Research Fund, 1973. 74 pp. index. plastic/spiral $3.
Recipe Index: Diabetic.

The revised and enlarged edition of the very popular *Diabetic Cooking Made Easy* appeared under the aegis of a new sponsor and publisher in 1973. The author, who is both a diabetic and a dietitian, offers a wealth of practical and imaginative suggestions for preparing diabetic meals and snacks, and for saving time in the kitchen. Unfortunately, the lack of subtitles and an all-inclusive index make it a bit difficult to locate and utilize all of the tips and informal recipes contained in the section on cooking hints. Desserts and salads comprise most of the formal recipes, with a few for meat, eggs, and sandwiches. Special sections discuss calculation of calories and carbohydrates in foods, the use of kitchen appliances, parties, convenience foods, and diabetic exchange values for brand name products.

brand name information	freezing	recipes: 75
convenience foods	lunches, packed	calories
entertaining	measurements: metric/	diabetic exchanges
food value charts & tables	household	servings
brand name information		sweeteners, artificial
diabetic exchanges		

106 Strachan, Clarice B. THE DIABETIC'S COOKBOOK. Medical Arts Publishing Foundation, 1972. 304 pp. index. paper $3.95.
Recipe Index: Diabetic.

One of the first cookbooks to use the exchange system for implementing diabetic diets, Strachan's book has gone through 14 printings since its original publication in 1955. More than a collection of recipes, it serves as a well-organized kitchen handbook for the diabetic. Extensive exchange lists, a sample diet plan, and generous space for noting the individual's dietary prescription comprise the introductory material. Recipes are grouped in two ways: according to the six diabetic exchange lists and according to conventional headings such as beverages, cakes, etc. The author encourages the cook to analyze and adapt her own recipes to the prescribed diet by providing workbook-like forms in each recipe section for additional recipes. These personal notations are facilitated by the inclusion of tables of food values and instructions for finding the proximate composition of food material.

bibliography	meal plans	diabetic exchanges
food value charts & tables	measurements: metric/	fat: total
calories	household	protein
carbohydrates	recipes: 200	servings
diabetic exchanges	calories	sweeteners, artificial
fat: total	carbohydrates	
protein		

107 Bowen, Angela J.M., M.D. THE DIABETIC GOURMET. Harper & Row, 1970. 155 pp. index. hard $6.95.
Recipe Index: Diabetic.

In addition to her medical research on diabetes, the author has served on the Food and Nutrition Committee of the American Diabetes Association and is past president of the Washington (state) Diabetes Association. Both weighed diets and exchange diets are explained, as well as general nutrition, controlled-fat diets, and special problems of meal planning. The recipes are reasonably varied and simple enough for the average cook; emphasis is on foods high in polyunsaturated fats. Care has been taken with the recipes since most of them carry additional comments on how to purchase particular ingredients, variations for those attempting to restrict calories or fat, etc. Emergency liquid and soft diet recipes are given. A special chapter instructs the cook in revising and creating recipes to suit the diabetic's prescription. Brand name information is provided on artificial sweeteners, and the appendix lists diabetes associations throughout the United States.

beverages, alcoholic	fat: total	diabetic exchanges
brand name information	protein	fat: total
entertaining	guest dining	protein
food value charts & tables	meal plans	servings
calories	recipes: 140	restaurant dining
carbohydrates	carbohydrates	sweeteners, artificial
diabetic exchanges		

108 Jones, Jeanne. THE CALCULATING COOK. 101 Productions, 1972. 192 pp. index. illus. hard $6.95; paper $3.95.
Recipe Index: Diabetic.

The author had long been a serious student of cookery when she learned that she was diabetic. With the assistance of dietitians, she adapted many of her favorite recipes to fit the requirements of a calculated diet. This attractive book's purpose is to enable the diabetic cook to entertain well, and to enjoy the more elaborate dishes that might ordinarily be left out of a restricted food plan. The scope of recipes is truly international, and reflects the author's particular expertise in Mexican and French cuisine. The categories range from basic stocks and soups through meats to desserts, breads, and beverages. The gourmet cook will find excellent supplementary information. Exchange lists include such forgotten foods as alfalfa sprouts, buffalo meat, and poi. Numerous cheeses are listed, and a special list covers the caloric and carbohydrate values for wines, liqueurs, and spirits. Complete three-day menus outline nine diets from 800 to 3000 calories. Uniquely helpful is the section "Have a Diabetic to Dinner," which tells just what to do, or not to do, when inviting a diabetic guest to dine. Brand name information concerns sugar substitutes.

beverages, alcoholic	menus: everyday, holiday	diabetic exchanges
brand name information	recipes: 190	servings
entertaining	calories	sweeteners, artificial
food value charts & tables		
diabetic exchanges		

109 Maddox, Gaynor. COOKBOOK FOR DIABETICS. Compiled by Ontario Dietetic Assn., and Canadian Diabetic Assn. Taplinger, 1967. 150 pp. illus. paper $1.95.

Originally prepared for Canadian diabetics, this book unexpectedly became popular in the United States. The publishers prepared a new edition for the American market by adapting certain common food terms, market and kitchen measurements, and cooking methods used in the United States. The editor is a regular contributor of food and nutrition articles to *Today's Health*, a publication of the American Medical Association. The exchange lists are those published by the U.S. Public Health Service. A complete cookbook of everyday recipes, it is especially helpful for beginner cooks. Numerous cooking terms are defined, and the book makes practical suggestions for preparing vegetables individually or in combination with others. Casserole dishes and sandwiches each receive a separate chapter. Recipes for relishes and pickles are included. In view of the fine recipe collection, the absence of an index is regrettable.

It should be noted that the contents of this book are very similar to the Canadian Diabetic Association and Canadian Dietetic Association's *Cookbook for Diabetics and all the Family* (2nd ed., 1972). The books are not interchangeable, however, since the Canadian and U.S. exchange systems differ. Identical recipes in the two cookbooks sometimes show different exchange values. For this reason, the original Canadian book is not included in this reference work.

canning	food value charts & tables	recipes: 250
convenience foods	diabetic exchanges	diabetic exchanges
food lists	freezing	servings
permitted	glossary	seasonings
	measurements: metric/	sweeteners, artificial
	household	

110 Bennett, Margaret. THE PERIPATETIC DIABETIC. Hawthorn, 1969, 338 pp. index. hard $8.95; paper $3.95.
Recipe Index: Diabetic.

The pseudonym Bennett includes two California librarian-authors, Barbara Toohey and June Biermann; the latter is a diabetic. The witty and delightful text would be a morale booster to any diabetic or friend of one. The first half of the book is advice by anecdote and the second half is devoted to gourmet cookery. Of the books reviewed, it gives the most extensive and practical information for traveling in the United States and overseas: names and addresses of diabetic associations abroad; foreign trade names for diabetic medical supplies; emergency medical information directions ("I am a diabetic," etc.) translated into 13 foreign languages; detailed advice on domestic and foreign airline meals. In the cookery section exchange lists contain an exceptionally large selection of convenience foods, especially brand name frozen foods, soups, sauces, salad dressings, kosher products, and canned dinners. Unfortunately, charm triumphs over clarity in the presentation of recipes; a second reading often is necessary to learn the yield and exchanges. Nonetheless, it is the only book in the diabetic category that can honestly be called fascinating.

beverages, alcoholic	food value charts & tables	guest dining
brand name information	brand name products	recipes: 50
convenience foods	diabetic exchanges	diabetic exchanges
		restaurant dining

111 Shadyside Hospital. DELIGHTFUL DIABETIC DINING. 1973. 35 pp. index. illus. paper $2. postpaid.
Recipe Index: Diabetic.

In a very pleasing format, dietitians at Shadyside Hospital have assembled a nicely varied selection of recipes, with several holiday, special occasion, and picnic suggestions. The introduction contains an educational quiz on weight loss and tips for adhering to the diabetic food plan. Menus for 1000 and 1200 calories are included. Brand name information encompasses artificial sweeteners and a few miscellaneous foods. Supplementary exchange lists include such items as Dutch pretzels, frozen waffles, and pizza.

brand name information	brand name information	recipes: 90
convenience foods	diabetic exchanges	diabetic exchanges
entertaining	lunches, packed	servings
food value charts & tables	menus: everyday, holiday	restaurant dining
		sweeteners, artificial

112 Charleston District Dietetic Assn. DINING DELECTABLES FOR THE DIABETIC. Medical University Hospital, 1973. 84 pp. illus. plastic spiral/paper $3.25 postpaid.

An all-round cookbook for the diabetic, this joint effort of five dietitians is particularly good for regional specialties of South Carolina. In addition to Charleston gumbo, jambalaya, and sweet potato soufflé, the recipe collection includes several "low country" favorites, such as she-crab soup, okra and tomato soup, and red rice with ham or shrimp. The total available glucose values have been calculated and presented with the recipes, besides the usual diabetic exchanges and gram weight measurements. The exchange lists include many brand name products, with emphasis on TV dinners, canned spaghetti, macaroni, stew, pork and beans, and some frozen convenience foods. Do's and don'ts of restaurant dining and tips for picnics are included. The book's only real limitation is the so-called "index" printed in the back of the book. Actually, it is a nonalphabetized table of contents and of little use in locating recipes.

brand name information	recipes: 140	glucose: total available
convenience foods	calories	protein
food value charts & tables	carbohydrates	servings
brand name products	diabetic exchanges	restaurant dining
diabetic exchanges	fat: total (teaspoons)	
glucose: total available		

113 Revell, Dorothy Tompkins, R.D. GOURMET RECIPES FOR DIABETICS: THE INTERNATIONAL DIABETIC DIET BOOK. Charles C. Thomas, 1971. 181 pp. index. hard $9.50.
Recipe Index: Diabetic.

The author is a registered dietitian who has written several books on diet cookery. The strength of this book lies in the thoroughness with which the author approaches food preparation for the diabetic. Material not usually found in similar books includes calculations for protein, fat,and carbohydrate requirements; calculation of the diet into the exchange list; carbohydrate distribution; distress situations with carbohydrate replacement; and available glucose replacement. Moreover, guidelines are provided for modifying the fat and cholesterol content of the diet. The exchange lists are quite extensive, and include a large number of infant and brand name convenience foods (the latter much the same as lists in entry 112, *Dining Delectables for the Diabetic*). The section on household and metric weights and measures is far more complete than average. Because many of the recipes in the well-varied collection were contributed by dietitians around the world, most will be new to the typical cook, and not the time-worn favorites so often included. As with many books of this type, however, the index is not properly arranged.

beverages, alcoholic	height/weight charts	diabetic exchanges
bibliography	meal plans	fat: total
brand name information	measurements: metric/	protein
convenience foods	household	servings
food value charts & tables	recipes: 90	references
brand name information	carbohydrates	seasonings
diabetic exchanges		

Supplementary Books

For additional supplementary information on diabetic diets *see* Calorie-restricted diets: 29, 51; Fat-controlled diets: 59; Multiple diets: 172; Food composition and values: 177, 178, 179, 180, 181.

114 Gormican, Annette, Ph.D. CONTROLLING DIABETES WITH DIET. Charles C. Thomas, 1971. 211 pp. illus. plastic spiral/paper $6.75.

Written by a medical nutritionist, this book answers questions that diabetics and their families most often ask regarding diet and nutrition. Nearly every aspect of eating is discussed, and the presentation is first-rate. Each brief, well-illustrated chapter is concluded with a summary and an informative question-and-answer review. Obviously aware of the need for time-saving shortcuts in the kitchen, the author includes one of the largest exchange lists for TV dinners, snacks, canned dinners, frozen entrées, cake mixes, and kosher food products. Readers are also instructed in the preparation of their own diabetic convenience meals. Other exchange lists are provided for sodium-restricted, fat-controlled (called fat-restricted in this book), and bland low-fiber (fiber-restricted) diets. Weight control is a primary topic in the book.

Information on summer camps for diabetic children, associations for diabetics, and meal plans for 1200 to 3500 calorie diets are included. Regrettably, there is no index to assist the reader in locating information in this outstanding book.

beverages, alcoholic	guest dining	restaurant dining
brand name information	height/weight charts	seasonings
convenience foods	lunches, packed	sweeteners, artificial
food value charts & tables	meal plans	youth diets
brand name products	recipes: 5	
diabetic exchanges		

115 Rosenthal, Helen, and Rosenthal, Jospeh, M.D. DIABETIC CARE IN PIC-
TURES. 4th ed. Lippincott, 1968. 227 pp. index. 105 illus. hard $6.50.

First published in 1946 and revised several times since, this book's longevity
eloquently testifies to its undisputed usefulness. The authors draw heavily on their
experiences as a nutritionist and as a physician in private practice and in a diabetes
clinic. Nearly half the text concerns food, the remainder hygiene and medical treatment for diabetics. It is profusely illustrated. The illustrated exchange lists, in particular, are truly instructive. Modifications are outlined for liquid, low-residue (fiber-
restricted), bland, and sodium-restricted diabetic diets.

beverages, alcoholic	carbohydrates	meal plans
brand name information	diabetic exchanges	recommended dietary allow-
convenience foods	fat: total	ances (RDA)
food value charts & tables	protein	seasonings
brand name information	glossary	sweeteners, artificial
calories	height/weight charts	youth diets

116 Fischer, Alfred E., M.D., and Horstmann, Dorothea L., R.D., M.A. A HAND-
BOOK FOR THE YOUNG DIABETIC. 4th ed. Intercontinental Medical Book
Corp., 1972. 76 pp. index. paper $4.75.
Recipe Index: Diabetic.

Previously published as *A Handbook for Diabetic Children*, this book has under-
gone several revisions since it first appeared in 1954. The authors are a pediatrician
specializing in diabetic care and a professor of nutrition. Most of the text is devoted
to diet; one chapter covers cookery, with a few others on hygiene and medical treatment. The authors' intent is to enable the young diabetic to lead a normal life. Information is given on summer camps in the United States, Canada, and Europe.

bibliography	recipes: 40
food value charts & tables	diabetic exchanges
diabetic exchanges	youth diets
menus: everyday	

117 McDonald, Mary B., R.D. A DIABETIC DIET? A PROGRAMMED
COURSE TEACHING DIET FOR THE DIABETIC. Univ. of Iowa Hospitals,
1971. 66 pp. spiral/paper $2.

This unusual book, printed in very large type, is a programmed course for teaching the do's and don'ts of diet for diabetics on an elementary level. The practical and
the theoretical are nicely interwoven in a format that both challenges and rewards
the reader. A painless but effective way to learn the fundamentals and their application, the book covers exchange lists and such special problems as sick days and fat-
controlled diets.

beverages, alcoholic
food lists
  permitted
  restricted

food value charts & tables
  diabetic exchanges
guest dining
lunches, packed

meal plans
menus: everyday
restaurant dining
sweeteners, artificial

Brochures and Product-Related Materials

118 American Dietetic Assn., and American Diabetes Assn. MEAL PLANNING WITH EXCHANGE LISTS. 1956. 20 pp. illus. paper $.15.

This standard booklet explains diabetic exchange lists with simple illustrations and a small collection of recipes.

food lists
  permitted
  restricted

food value charts & tables
  diabetic exchanges

recipes: 20
  diabetic exchanges
  servings

119 American Diabetes Assn. FORECAST REPRINT SERIES. 4–8 pp. illus. paper $.10; $.25/3.

Major authoritative articles offering practical advice have been reprinted from the ADA *Forecast* magazine. The following series numbers are the same as the American Diabetes Association's for ordering:

9. When Diabetics Have Ulcers
10. Meals on Wheels
12. Food Values for Passover Dishes
15. The Food We Eat
16. The Six Exchange Lists
17. The Child with Diabetes
22. Canning Fruits Without Sugar
26. Sugar Substitutes: Statement on Saccharin
28. Healthy Babies for Diabetic Mothers
31. All about Calories
32. Traveling with Diabetes
34. The High Cost of Proteins
35. Available Carbohydrates of Vegetables and Fruits
36. Obesity
37. Vary Your Diet with Food Exchanges
44. The Seven Wonders of a Slice of Bread
50. Exercise, Calories, and Diabetes
53. Protein: Its Nature and Its Importance

120 Good Housekeeping. COOKBOOK FOR DIABETICS: 125 FAVORITE RECIPES. Hearst, 1968. 67 pp. paper $.50 prepaid.

A well-varied selection of recipes from soups through main dishes to desserts.

canning
freezing
menus: holiday
recipes: 125

calories
diabetic exchanges
servings
sweeteners, artificial

121 Prater, Barbara M., M.S., R.D.; Denton, Nancy J., R.D.; and Oakeson, Kathleen F., R.D. FOOD AND YOU, NUTRITION IN DIABETES. Diabetes Center, 1970. 48 pp. illus. paper $3.

An unusually bright and colorful guide to nutrition and the diabetic exchange lists.

convenience foods
food lists
  permitted
  restricted

food value charts & tables
  diabetic exchanges
guest dining
sweeteners, artificial

122 Cinnamon, Pamela A., M.Sc., P. Dt., and Swanson, Marilyn A., M.S., R.D. EVERYTHING YOU ALWAYS WANTED TO KNOW* ABOUT EX-CHANGE VALUES FOR FOODS (*BUT WERE UNABLE TO FIND OUT!). University Cities Diabetes Education Program, 1973. 32 pp. paper $1. prepaid.

One of the most complete exchange lists for brand name and convenience foods; includes Japanese-American foods and textured vegetable protein (TVP) exchanges.

beverages, alcoholic	food value charts & tables	measurements: metric/
bibliography	brand name information	household
brand name information	diabetic exchanges	
convenience foods		

123 Eli Lilly and Co. DAILY MENU GUIDE. 1972. single page. free. Also available in Spanish (entry 137).

Meal plans and menus printed on a large single sheet. Separate sheets available for 1200, 1500, 1800, 2000, 2500, and 3000 calories.

food lists	food value charts & tables	meal plans
permitted	diabetic exchanges	menus: everyday
restricted		

124 Eli Lilly and Co. DIET PLANNER. 1972. 43 pp. paper free.

Pocket-size booklet with meal plans and menus for six diets, 1200 to 3000 calories, and exchange lists.

food lists	food value charts & tables	menus: everyday
permitted	diabetic exchanges	
restricted	meal plans	

125 Lutheran General Hospital. CONVENIENCE FOODS FOR CALCULATED DIETS. 1970. 18 pp. paper $1. prepaid.

Exchange lists for hundreds of convenience foods, listed by brand names.

brand name information	food value charts & tables
convenience foods	brand name information
	diabetic exchanges

126 Abiaka, Monica H., R.D. JAPANESE-AMERICAN FOOD EQUIVALENTS FOR CALCULATING EXCHANGE DIETS. American Dietetic Assn. 1973. 8 pp. paper $.65.

This reprint from the *Journal of the American Dietetic Association* presents a detailed discussion of foods eaten by Japanese-Americans, and gives comprehensive exchange lists.

food lists	carbohydrates	protein
permitted	diabetic exchanges	sodium
food value charts & tables	fat: total	references
calories	potassium	

127 Labrenz, Janice Bate. PLANNING MEALS FOR THE BACKPACKER WITH DIABETES—NUTRITIONAL VALUES OF FREEZE-DRIED FOODS. American Dietetic Assn., 1972. 7 pp. illus. paper $.65.

This reprint from the *Journal of the American Dietetic Association* discusses meal-planning for backpacking, with an analysis of freeze-dried foods available in the Pacific Northwest (many brands also distributed nationally).

brand name information	fat: total	carbohydrates
convenience foods	protein	fat
food value charts & tables	lunches, packed	protein
brand name information	meal plans	servings
calories	menus: everyday	references
carbohydrates	recipes: 2	

128 Diabetes Education Center. EXCHANGES FOR SPECIAL OCCASIONS. 1972. 24 pp. illus. paper $1. prepaid.

Menus, recipes, and exchange lists for such special occasions as childrens parties, Christmas, Easter, Thanksgiving, and picnics.

beverages, alcoholic	food value charts & tables	diabetic exchanges
brand name information	diabetic exchanges	servings
entertaining	menus: holiday	restaurant dining
food lists	recipes: 10	seasonings
permitted		youth diets

129 Diabetes Education Center. FRUIT FIX-UPS. 1971. 31 pp. illus. paper $1.50 prepaid.

A cookbook that features not only fruit recipes but several for cookies, beverages, and jellies as well.

canning	recipes: 65
food value charts & tables	diabetic exchanges
diabetic exchanges	servings
	sweeteners, artificial

130 Diabetes Education Center. MENU MAGIC WITH EXCHANGES. 1972. 61 pp. illus. paper $1.50 prepaid.

Cookbook of everyday fare, with emphasis on meats and main dishes.

recipes: 60
  diabetic exchanges
  servings

131 North Suburban Dietetic Assn. of Illinois. YOUR FOOD EXCHANGE PLAN. 1972. illus. plastic $1. prepaid.

A colorful personal meal plan and exchange list printed on a large plastic folder.

food lists	food value charts & tables
permitted	diabetic exchanges
restricted	

132 USV Pharmaceutical Corp. AMERICAN DIABETIC DIET. 1971. single page. illus. free.

Abbreviated exchange list and sample menu for typical American diet. (A similar format is used in entries 133, 139-143.)

food lists	food value charts & tables
permitted	diabetic exchanges
restricted	menus: everyday

133 USV Pharmaceutical Corp. SOUTHERN AMERICAN "SOUL" DIABETIC DIET. 1971. single page. illus. free.

Abbreviated exchange list and sample menu for typical "soul food" diabetic diet.

food lists
  permitted
  restricted

food value charts & tables
  diabetic exchanges
  menus: everyday

134 Campbell Soup Co. NUTRITION: WHY IS IT IMPORTANT? 1973. 27 pp. paper. free.

Basic introduction to nutrition, with exchange lists for manufacturer's brand name soups, frozen dinners, and canned products.

brand name information
convenience foods
food value charts & tables
  brand name information
  calories

carbohydrates
diabetic exchanges
fat: total
protein

sodium
vitamins/minerals
recommended dietary allowances (RDA)
references

135 Worthington Foods. MEATLESS MENU PLANNING FOR DIABETIC AND WEIGHT CONTROL PROGRAMS. illus. single page. free.

Folder containing diabetic exchange lists for manufacturer's textured vegetable protein (TVP) foods as well as other foods, and menus for 1000, 1200, 1500, and 1800 calorie diets.

brand name information
food lists
  permitted
food value charts & tables

brand name information
calories
carbohydrates
diabetic exchanges

fat: total
protein
menus: everyday

Foreign Language Materials

136 Los Angeles District, California Dietetic Assn. LA DIETA DIABETICA (THE DIABETIC DIET). 1973. 21 pp. paper $1. single copy; $.50 additional copies.

Mexican-American diabetic diet with exchange lists and a few recipes, all in both English and Spanish.

food lists
  permitted
  restricted

food value charts & tables
  diabetic exchanges
recipes: 5
  diabetic exchanges

137 Eli Lilly and Co. GUÍA DEL MENÚ DIARIO (DAILY MENU GUIDE). 1972. single page. free.

Large single sheets with Spanish exchange lists and menus for 1200, 1500, 1800, 2000, 2500, and 3000 calorie diets. Translation of entry 123 rather than special list of Mexican-American or Puerto Rican foods.

food lists
  permitted
  restricted

food value charts & tables
  diabetic exchanges
meal plans
menus: everyday

138 New York Community Service Society. DIABETES: 1500 CALORIE DIET. 1973. 14 pp. illus. paper $.20 prepaid; $.15 for 100 or more.

Chinese-American exchange lists and meal plans printed in both English and Chinese.

food lists	food value charts & tables	meal plans
permitted	diabetic exchanges	menus: everyday
restricted		

139 USV Pharmaceutical Corp. CHINESE DIABETIC DIET. 1971. single page. illus. free.

Abbreviated exchange list and sample menu for Chinese-American diabetic diet; printed in English on front and Chinese on reverse side.

food lists	food value charts & tables
permitted	diabetic exchanges
restricted	menus: everyday

140 USV Pharmaceutical Corp. ITALIAN-AMERICAN DIABETIC DIET. 1971. single page. illus. free.

Abbreviated exchange list and sample menu for Italian-American diabetic diet; printed in English on front and Italian on reverse side.

food lists	food value charts & tables
permitted	diabetic exchanges
restricted	menus: everyday

141 USV Pharmaceutical Corp. JEWISH DIABETIC DIET. 1971. single page. illus. free.

Abbreviated exchange list and sample menu for Jewish-American diabetic diet; printed in English on front and Yiddish on reverse side.

food lists	food value charts & tables
permitted	diabetic exchange lists
restricted	menus: everyday

142 USV Pharmaceutical Corp. MEXICAN-AMERICAN DIABETIC DIET. 1971. single page. illus. free.

Abbreviated exchange list and sample menu for Mexican-American diabetic diet; printed in English on front and Spanish on reverse side.

food lists	food value charts & tables
permitted	diabetic exchanges
restricted	menus: everyday

143 USV Pharmaceutical Corp. PUERTO RICAN DIABETIC DIET. 1971. single page. illus. free.

Abbreviated exchange list and sample menu for Puerto Rican diabetic diet; printed in English on front and Spanish on reverse side.

food lists	food value charts & tables
permitted	diabetic exchanges
restricted	menus: everyday

Periodicals

144 ADA FORECAST. American Diabetes Assn. bi-monthly. $3/yr.

This small magazine, written for diabetics and their families, carries a regular feature on diabetic cookery. Good recipes are given each month, with the exchanges and diabetic gram weights. Many of the recipes in past issues have been reprinted in Behrman's popular book, *A Cookbook for Diabetics* (entry 104).

H.
Protein Modifications

H-1. Gluten-Restricted Diets

Gluten is a protein component found in wheat, barley, oats, and rye. Persons with gluten-induced enteropathy (or celiac disease) or nontropical sprue are unable to tolerate the gliadin fraction of gluten because of a malabsorption syndrome (the inability of the small intestine to absorb nutrients completely and properly). The four offending cereals, as well as many food products derived from them, are restricted. Books annotated in this section deal exclusively with gluten-restricted diets, but many additional gluten-restricted recipes can be found in allergy diet cookbooks and in multiple diet cookbooks. Such recipes are clearly labeled gluten-free. and the recipe sources can be seen at a glance in the chart (Fig. 1) presented at the beginning of Part I-A, Allergy Diets.

Since the problem of wheat, barley, oat, and rye intolerance associated with celiac disease and nontropical sprue is clearly related to a protein factor, gluten-restricted diets are classified as protein modifications rather than as allergy diets, a term that usually implies that the source of the problem is not so precisely pinpointed. Obviously, gluten-restricted diets overlap barley-, oat-, rye-, and wheat-free allergy diets. Wheat-free allergy recipes that do not include barley, oats, rye, or their derivatives can be used by those on gluten-restricted diets. Conversely, gluten-restricted recipes can be used by those on wheat-, barley-, oat-, or rye-free allergy diets.

For supplementary information on gluten-restricted diets *see* Multiple diets: 171.

Cookbooks

For additional gluten-restricted recipes *see* Allergy diets: 5; Protein-restricted diets: 163, 164; Multiple diets: 167, 168, 173, 176.

145 Wood, Marion N. GOURMET FOOD ON A WHEAT-FREE DIET. Charles C. Thomas, 1967. 112 pp. index. hard $5.95.
Recipe Index: Gluten-restricted.

The author, who has now written two gluten-free cookbooks, was motivated to begin her experimentation and research when her husband was placed on a gluten-restricted diet, and she could find few recipes suitable for her purposes. Because non-gluten flours lack elasticity, cooks will meet with failure if they attempt to bake without a reliable guide. Readers will be encouraged by Ms. Wood's account of her struggle to develop tasty substitutes for her favorite nonwheat flour recipes in the small and remote town of Globe, Arizona. An introductory chapter warns the dieter of such hidden sources of gluten as root beer and cream cheese. A table lists foods to be avoided or used as substitutes; a few brand names are mentioned. Wheat, rice, and soy food values are compared in the appendix. The recipe collection concentrates on baked goods, and includes everything from cookies and cream puffs to bread, blintzes, and gingerbread waffles. One chapter covers main dishes.

brand name information	food value charts & tables	recipes: 170
convenience foods	calcium	servings
food lists	calories	references
permitted	protein	restaurant dining
restricted	glossary	

146 Sheedy, Charlotte Baum, and Keifetz, Norman. COOKING FOR YOUR CELIAC CHILD. Dial, 1969. 244 pp. index. hard $5.95.
Recipe Index: Gluten-restricted.

Ms. Sheedy is a cookbook editor who collaborated with a group of mothers of celiac children in collecting, adapting, and testing the book's recipes; her collaborator, Keifetz, is a medical writer. Supplementing the recipes is a substantial introduction that describes the celiac syndrome and offers practical suggestions for coping with problems that arise from denying small children so many normal foods. A list of substitutes for gluten cereal grains and flours with their equivalencies and characteristics is provided. The recipe collection is broad, ranging from soups and main dishes through desserts, and the organization of material is good. Most of the dishes would be appropriate for all family members, but there is a good selection of treats for children, such as pretzels, noodles, brownies, ice cream, and cookies. All recipes are gluten-free; some others are starch-free, sugar-free, low-fat, no-fat, or combinations of these, according to the introduction. Aside from noting where fat can be omitted, or when slight modifications can be made, the recipes are not otherwise identified or separately indexed when they fall into a low-fat or starch-free category.

bibliography	permitted	references
brand name information	restricted	sweeteners, artificial
convenience foods	recipes: 330	youth diets
food lists	servings	

147 Hjortland, Marthana, M.S.; Abowd, Margaret M.; Birk, Allene, R.N.; Hinshaw, Deanna; and French, Arthur B., M.D. LOW GLUTEN DIET WITH TESTED RECIPES. Univ. of Michigan Medical Center, 1969. 66 pp. illus. paper $1. Also includes copy of SOME PACKAGED AND PREPARED FOOD ALLOWED ON A MODIFIED GLUTEN DIET.
Recipe Index: Gluten-restricted.

Long a popular book in this category, this title first appeared in 1958 and has been revised five times since. A special chapter on the principles of a low-gluten diet explains the types and amounts of flour that can be substituted for wheat flour. Numerous cooking hints explain how other ingredients react with low-gluten flours. Recipes are restricted to those that would normally call for wheat flour: yeast breads, quick breads, cookies, desserts, and selected main dishes. Several dishes from Brazil are given in the Latin American chapter. The absence of an index is regrettable, but the table of contents is a reasonable substitute. Only a few recipe ingredients are identified by brand name in the cookbook, but the supplement, *Some Packaged and Prepared Food Allowed on a Modified Gluten Diet* (entry 148), which is provided free, is very specific on acceptable brand name foods, mixes, and convenience foods.

bibliography	food lists	recipes: 70
brand name information	permitted	servings
convenience foods	restricted	

148 Univ. of Michigan Medical Center. SOME PACKAGED AND PREPARED FOOD ALLOWED ON A MODIFIED GLUTEN DIET. Univ. of Michigan Medical Center, 1973. 7 pp. paper $1. separate; free with Hjortland book.

This supplement, which can be ordered separately from the Hjortland title (entry 147), is a long list of nationally available brand name products suitable for a modified gluten diet. A list of mail-order houses is included. The types of foods covered are flours and breads, cereals, crackers and snacks, pasta, puddings, dessert mixes, toppings and frostings, coffee creamers, salad dressings, ice creams, baking powder, canned entrées, luncheon meats, cheeses, soups, candies, frozen vegetables, beverages, and condiments. The format has been kept very simple and inexpensive to allow frequent updating.

brand name information	convenience foods	youth diets

149 Carpenter, Carolyn Busbee. LUNCHEON WITH LAURIE. Carolyn Busbee Carpenter, 1973. 96 pp. paper $2.50.
Recipe Index: Gluten-restricted.

A pleasant and practical book written by the mother of a celiac child, this title has a down-to-earth quality. First published when the author's daughter, Laurie, was a very small child, this second edition has been revised and now contains some honest but encouraging comments about the recipes and her gluten-free diet from the grown-up Laurie who is now a teenager. As with some of the other books in this category, there are a number of tips for cooking with nonwheat flours. The author notes that some of the recipes contain oats, which are not permitted in some modified gluten diets. The variety of recipes is good, covering breads, cakes, cookies, desserts, and a large number of main dishes. The lack of an index makes it difficult to locate some of the truly useful recipes, such as pizza, ice cream cones, and pancakes.

brand name information	food lists	lunches, packed
convenience foods	restricted	recipes: 220
	freezing	youth diets

150 Wood, Marion N. DELICIOUS AND EASY RICE FLOUR RECIPES. Charles C. Thomas, 1972. 137 pp. index. spiral/paper $5.50.
Recipe Index: Gluten-restricted.

This second book on gluten-free cookery by Marion Wood is a worthy successor to her first title. Although all the recipes are wheat-, rye-, barley-, and oat-free, the collection is not strictly limited to rice flour recipes. The chapter on Mexican food, for example, includes a number of corn- or bean-based recipes. There is excellent variety among recipes for soups, breads, pancakes, crêpes, cream puffs, cakes, pastries, sauces, and main dishes. Both an American and an international flavor are discernible. Chapters are introduced with helpful explanations of any special problems that may be encountered in gluten-free cookery.

brand name information recipes: 240
convenience foods servings

151 The Hospital for Sick Children. CELIAC DISEASE. 1968. 87 pp. index. illus. paper $1.65 postpaid. Also available in French and Italian (entries 152 and 153). *Recipe Index:* Gluten-restricted.

This attractive, well-organized cookbook opens with an explanation of celiac disease and a description of the gluten-free diet. Suggestions are given for cooking with low-gluten flours and for keeping baked goods fresh. A guide to the substitution of low-gluten for ordinary wheat flours is provided. The authors note that the book contains recipes using oats, which some diets exclude. The recipe collection is divided into chapters covering breads, cakes, candies, cookies, desserts, main dishes, and muffins, and is very good in its coverage of gluten-free substitutes for many childhood favorites. Although of Canadian origin, this book would be a welcome addition in any American kitchen where gluten-free meals are prepared.

food lists recipes: 145
  permitted servings
  restricted youth diets
meal plans

Foreign Language Materials

152 The Hospital for Sick Children. LA MALADIE CÉLIAQUE (CELIAC DISEASE). 1968. 87 pp. index. illus. paper $1.65 postpaid. Also available in English and Italian.

This book is a French translation of *Celiac Disease Recipes* (entry 151).

153 The Hospital for Sick Children. MALATTIA CELIACA RICETTE (CELIAC DISEASE RECIPES). 1968. 87 pp. index. illus. paper $1.65 postpaid. Also available in French and English.

This book is an Italian translation of *Celiac Disease Recipes* (entry 151).

H-2. Phenylalanine-Restricted Diets

Phenylalanine is an essential amino acid, or basic component of protein, which is found in meat, fish, dairy products, and grains. The inability to metabolize phenylalanine completely is an inherited disorder, phenylketonuria, commonly known as PKU. Unless the intake of phenylalanine is restricted during the earliest years of life, affected individuals suffer severe mental retardation. Phenylalanine is present in many ordinary foods, so these diets rely heavily upon pharmaceutically prepared food supplements.

For phenylalanine-restricted recipes *see* Protein-restricted diets: 164; Multiple diets: 171, 173, 174, 175, 176.

Supplementary Books

154 Lyman, Frank L., M.D. PHENYLKETONURIA. Charles C. Thomas, 1963. 318 pp. index. illus. hard $12.75.
Recipe Index: Phenylalanine-restricted.

Essentially a medical book, this title is included for its sizable chapter on phenylalanine-restricted recipes. Some 70 pages are devoted to diet and recipes, and a great deal of brand name information is given, not only for proprietary phenylalanine-restricted products but also for commonly available baby foods, cereals, puddings, and canned soups. The author uses a system of phenylalanine equivalents, or exchanges, in both the extensive food tables and in the recipes. The recipe collection incorporates material published in the *Journal of the American Dietetic Association* and in *Archives of Pediatrics;* others were created especially for this book. Soups, salads, main dishes, vegetables, sauces, dressings, breads, pastries, puddings, ice cream, and frozen treats are included. In summary, they are the type of foods that would appeal to children. Moreover, they make the cook's job as easy as possible by utilizing convenience foods whenever possible. It is regrettable that the recipes are not indexed in the book.

bibliography	brand name products	recipes: 110
brand name information	calories	calories
convenience foods	phenylalanine	phenylalanine exchanges
food value charts & tables	phenylalanine exchanges	references
		youth diets

155 Beto, Judy A., and Holli, Betsy B., R.D. COOKIE FOR A LOW-PHENYLALANINE DIET. American Dietetic Assn., 1974. single page. $.30.
Recipe Index: Phenylalanine-restricted.

This reprint from the *Journal of the American Dietetic Association* presents a cookie recipe utilizing strained bananas that the authors feel will be acceptable to the entire family.

convenience foods	phenylalanine	references
recipes: 1	servings	youth diets

156 Rincic, Margery Mallory, and Rogers, Patricia J., Ph.D. A LOW-PROTEIN, LOW-PHENYLALANINE VEGETABLE CASSEROLE. American Dietetic Assn., 1969. 4 pp. paper $.30.
Recipe Index: Phenylalanine-restricted.

This reprint from the *Journal of the American Dietetic Association* gives an entrée casserole that is acceptable not only to the phenylketonuric child but also to the entire family.

food value charts & tables	recipes: 1	protein
amino acids	calories	servings
nitrogen	phenylalanine	references
		youth diets

H–3. Protein-Restricted Diets

Protein-restricted diets collected in this chapter also restrict sodium and potassium, and all are associated with the treatment of kidney or renal disorders. Due to the development of the kidney machine and to the success of kidney transplants there is a growing number of persons who must cope with the long term consequences of limited kidney function. Since protein is the chief source of urea and acid wastes, its intake must be reduced and regulated so as not to overtax the kidneys in ridding the body of these substances. The diet calls for a reduction in the total amount of protein intake with emphasis on using protein of the highest biological value, that is protein containing all the essential amino acids such as that found in meat, eggs, and fish, rather than the incomplete proteins found in grains and cereals. Sodium and potassium are controlled for a variety of reasons and special attention must be given to the use of fruits and vegetables that are rich in potassium.

Cookbooks

For additional protein-restricted recipes *see* Multiple diets: 167, 168, 171, 173, 174, 175, 176.

157 Krawitt, Laura P, and Weinberger, Emily K. PRACTICAL LOW PROTEIN COOKERY. Charles C. Thomas, 1971. 110 pp. index. plastic spiral/paper $6.75. *Recipe Index:* Protein-restricted.

The most widely known cookbook devoted exclusively to low-protein cookery, this book has been compiled by two women with husbands on low-protein diets. Advice is given on careful measurement of foods, as well as on the proper use of specific ingredients, such as baking powder, flour, margarine, milk and cream substitutes, vinegar, and water. Detailed menus for a week include protein and caloric values for each meal and totals for each day. Recipe information is unusually detailed and complete. Each ingredient is analyzed for potassium, protein, and sodium; total quantities for these nutrients are given for each recipe, as well as the number of calories and the presence or absence of cholesterol. Comments on many recipes describe variations and the resulting food values. The book provides a small amount of brand name information in recipes and food tables.

bibliography	protein	potassium
brand name information	sodium	protein
food value charts & tables	menus: everyday	servings
brand name information	recipes: 85	sodium
calories	calories	references
potassium	cholesterol: present/	
	absent	

158 de St. Jeor, Sachiko T., M.S.; Carlston, Betty Jill; Christensen, Susan; Maddock, Robert K., Jr., M.D.; and Tyler, Frank H., M.D. LOW PROTEIN DIETS FOR THE TREATMENT OF CHRONIC RENAL FAILURE. Univ. of Utah Press, 1970. 71 pp. plastic spiral/paper $4.50. Equivalent list reprints available. *Recipe Index:* Protein-restricted.

Three research dietitians and two physicians collaborated in preparing this book directed at both the professional worker and the ambulatory patient. An index would have increased the usefulness of the book. Tabs, however, clearly mark the principal divisions: background for the physician, dietitian, and patient; protein equivalent lists; potassium equivalent lists; menus; recipes; and references. The equivalent, or exchange, lists for protein and potassium values were computer-calculated for use in the menu and recipe sections. About three-quarters of the recipes include a computer analysis of calories, potassium, protein, and sodium per 100 gram yield; the others give only exchange equivalent values. All measurements in menus and recipes are given in grams, but exchange lists use both metric and common household measurements.

brand name information	recipes: 85.	protein exchanges
food value charts & tables	calories	servings
potassium exchanges	potassium	sodium
protein exchanges	protein	references
menus: everyday		

159 Maryland Dietetic Assn., RENAL DIET COOKBOOK. 1973. 67 pp. index. paper $1. postpaid.
Recipe Index: Protein-restricted.

Prepared by the Diet Therapy Section of the Maryland Dietetic Association, this cookbook should be used with the companion booklet *Diet for Patients with Renal Disease* (entry 162) prepared by the same group. The recipes cover most types of foods, including breads, butters, desserts, eggs, fish, meats, salads, sauces, soups, and vegetables. All recipes contain information on both protein exchanges and pertinent food values; many also indicate the amount of fluid in cubic centimeters (cc.). The presentation of material is clear and to the point.

recipes: 75	potassium	servings
calories	protein	sodium
fluid, cc.	protein exchanges	seasonings

Supplementary Books

For additional supplementary information on protein-restricted diets *see* Food composition and values: 177, 178, 179, 180, 181.

160 Los Angeles District, California Dietetic Assn. A GUIDE TO PROTEIN CONTROLLED DIETS. 1973. 33 pp. paper $2. PATIENT'S GUIDE TO PROTEIN CONTROLLED DIETS available separately (entry 161).

Divided into three principal parts, this booklet provides food lists for dietitians and patients and sample meal patterns for 20, 40, 60, and 80 gram protein diets. There are no recipes. The professional section lists values for calories, potassium, protein, and sodium found in a variety of foods, brand name products, and specialty items; both grams and household measurements are used for portions. The patient's section consists of exchange lists for foods and sample meal patterns utilizing the exchange lists. Brand name cereals, candies, beverages, and low-protein products are discussed. The patient's section, which is available separately in either English or Spanish, includes some lists from the dietitian's section and a daily menu plan.

beverages, alcoholic	calories	meal plans
brand name information	potassium	references
food value charts & tables	protein	seasonings
brand name products	protein exchanges	
	sodium	

161 Los Angeles District, California Dietetic Assn. PATIENT'S GUIDE TO PROTEIN-CONTROLLED DIETS. 1973. 16 pp. paper $.25. Also available in Spanish (entry 166).

This reprint of the patient's portion of entry 160 provides a simple introduction to the protein-controlled diet, with a meal plan section to be filled in by the dietitian or physician. Most of the reprint is devoted to exchange lists.

beverages, alcoholic	calories	protein exchanges
food value charts & tables	potassium	sodium
brand name products	protein	meal plans
		seasonings

162 Maryland Dietetic Assn. DIET FOR PATIENTS WITH RENAL DISEASE (INCLUDING DIALYSIS). 1971. 21 pp. paper $1. postpaid.

As a practical guide to the protein-restricted diet, this booklet supplements *Renal Diet Cookbook* (entry 159). The introduction explains the role of protein, sodium, potassium, fluids, calories, vitamins, and minerals in the diet. Space is provided for the dietitian to note the patient's individual diet plan and sample menu. The bulk of the book is devoted to protein exchange lists, with measurements in both grams and household measurements. The reader is told how to dialyze vegetables and how to convert household and metric measurements of foods. Tips are given for eating out.

food lists	food value charts & tables	measurements: metric/
permitted	protein exchanges	household
restricted	lunches, packed	restaurant dining
		seasonings

Brochures and Product-Related Materials

163 Smith, Elizabeth B., Ph.D. GLUTEN-FREE BREADS FOR PATIENTS WITH UREMIA. American Dietetic Assn., 1971. 3 pp. illus. paper $.30.
Recipe Index: Protein-restricted.

This reprint from the *Journal of the American Dietetic Association* discusses the development of a recipe for gluten-free yeast bread that is low in potassium and sodium.

recipes: 1	protein
calories	servings
	references

164 Sorensen, Molly K. A YEAST-LEAVENED, LOW-PROTEIN, LOW-ELECTROLYTE BREAD. American Dietetic Assn., 1970. 3 pp. illus. paper $.30.
Recipe Index: Phenylalanine-restricted; Protein-restricted.

The bread recipe presented in this reprint from the *Journal of the American Dietetic Association* gives quantities for home baking as well as for institutional baking of a bread designed to satisfy the requirements of uremic patients and those with phenylketonuria (PKU).

recipes: 2
  servings
references

165 General Mills Chemicals. CAL-POWER® HIGH CALORIE BEVERAGE. 15 3 × 5 index cards. free.
Recipe Index: Protein-restricted.

Set of recipe cards gives soup and beverage recipes using manufacturer's brand name product.

brand name information	carbohyrates	protein
recipes: 12	fat: total	servings
calories	potassium	sodium

Foreign Language Material

166 Los Angeles District, California Dietetic Assn. UNA GUÍA PARA LAS PACIENTES POR LAS DIETAS DE PROTEÍNA LIMITADA. 1973. 16 pp. paper $.25. Also available in English (entry 161).

A Spanish translation of entry 161, this reprint covers the basic concepts of protein-restricted diets, provides space for a meal plan to be filled in by the professional, and lists dozens of foods in protein exchange lists.

beverages, alcoholic	calories	protein exchanges
food value charts & tables	potassium	sodium
brand name products	protein	meal plans
		seasonings

I.
Purine-Restricted Diets

Purine-restricted diets are associated with the treatment of gout. Medication, however, has supplanted diet therapy to a very wide extent. Purine-restricted diets limit the intake of purine by eliminating such purine-rich foods as liver, kidneys, dried legumes, and meat extracts.

For purine-restricted recipes *see* Multiple diets: 168, 169.

For supplementary information on purine-restricted diets *see* Multiple diets: 171, 172.

J.
Multiple Diets

Cookbooks

167 Salmon, Margaret B., R.D., M.S., and Quigley, Althea E., R.D. ENJOYING YOUR RESTRICTED DIET. Charles C. Thomas, 1972. 307 pp. index. illus. hard $10.75.
Recipe Index: Calorie-restricted; Diabetic; Fat-controlled; Gluten-restricted; Protein-restricted; Sodium-restricted.

Written by professional dietitians from New Jersey and New York, with contributions by 33 dietitian and physician collaborators, this attractive and thoughtfully organized book encompasses seven diets, including some for which there is little other information available to the lay person. Succinct, yet informative, each separate diet section is a model of what a diet cookbook should be. Introductory remarks by both a medical doctor and a registered dietitian explain the why and how of the diet. Complete menus are given for a week, plus many for holidays, totaling nearly 200. Restaurant and lunch box dining are covered, as well as brand name information, essential food value lists, exchanges, and cooking tips. As far as can be determined, this is the only book for nonprofessionals with information on the medium-chain triglyceride (MCT) diet.

brand name information
food lists, permitted
　gluten-free
food lists, restricted
　diabetic
　gluten-free
food value charts & tables
　calories
　carbohydrates
　diabetic exchanges
　fat: total
　potassium
　protein
　sodium

glossary: fat-controlled
lunches, packed
meal plans
menus: everyday/
　holiday
recipes, total: 300
　calorie-restricted: 25;
　　calories; servings
　cholesterol- and fat-
　　controlled: 35; fat:
　　total; servings
　diabetic: 85; exchanges;
　　servings
　gluten-free: 20; servings
　medium-chain triglyc-

　erides: 35; medium-
　　chain triglycerides;
　　long-chain triglyc-
　　erides; servings
　protein-, potassium-,
　　sodium-restricted: 40;
　　calories; potassium;
　　protein; sodium;
　　servings
　sodium-restricted: 45;
　　sodium
references
restaurant dining
seasonings: sodium-
　　restricted

168 Nilson, Bee. COOKING FOR SPECIAL DIETS, 2nd ed. Penguin, 1971. 459 pp. index. illus. paper $2.95.

Recipe Index: Fat-restricted; Fiber-restricted; Protein-restricted; Sodium-restricted.

A member of the British Dietetic Association, the author has written several other cookbooks, including the popular British classic *The Penguin Cookery Book*. Far-ranging in its scope of diets and recipes, the book is divided into two main sections: diets and recipes applicable to the diets. Some 30 diets are outlined. The typical sub-chapter for each diet discusses how the body is affected (with illustrations), modifications of the normal diet, foods to include or avoid, specialty foods, fitting in with family meals, cooking methods, meal patterns, eating out, and sandwich meals. Two weeks' menus are provided for the major diets. Menus refer to the nearly 600 numbered recipes in the second half of the book. Many recipes serve more than one diet, and the author has found 1900 applications for the 600 recipes. While very complete, the recipe collection necessarily includes British favorites rather than American ones. Diet identification is not provided for all of the recipes in the cookbook section, so the reader normally must proceed from the suggested diet menus to the numbered recipes. The only real limitation for American readers is the occasional confusion that may arise from British terminology for some ingredients (caster sugar, cornflour, sultanas). The wealth of brand name information primarily concerns products available in Great Britain, so an American edition of Nilson's book would be useful indeed. Metric equivalents are given for kitchen measurements, and the book provides separate diet and recipe indexes. The nature of the book's organization makes it difficult to include in the Recipe Index; however, a special effort has been made to index four different diets. Following are diets as listed in Nilson's table of contents, with the number of recipes in each category and information for each recipe in that category. Diets included in *The Diet Food Finder* are italicized.

General Diets
    Liquid or fluid diet: 150
    Semi-solid or soft diet: 170
    Light diet: 90
Diseases of the Digestive System
    Milk diet for ulcers: none
    Low-fiber diet (fiber-restricted): 125
    Gluten-free diet (gluten-restricted): 240
    High-fiber diet: 85
Diseases of the Liver, Gall Bladder, and Bile Duct
    Low-fat diet (fat-restricted): 200
Diabetes: 70; carbohydrates, grams
Overweight (calorie-restricted): 70; calories
Diseases of the Cardio-vascular or Circulatory System
    Low-sodium diet (sodium-restricted): 110
    Diet with modified or low animal-fat content (fat-controlled): 150
Diseases of the Kidneys and Urinary Tract
    Low-protein diet (protein-restricted): 50
    High-protein restricted-salt diet: none
Undernutrition (high-caloric): 200

Fevers and Infections
Anaemia: 65
Gout (purine-restricted): 90
Diseases of Childhood (*youth diets*)
Liquid or fluid diet
Semi-solid or soft diet
Mouth and throat: 10
Gastric and duodenal ulcers
Diarrhoea
Atonic constipation
Fevers and feverish colds: 20
Typhoid fever
Jaundice and cirrhosis
Over-weight
Diseases of the kidney
Dental caries
Undernutrition
Anaemia
Diet in Old Age (*geriatric diets*)

brand name information (British)
food lists, permitted
calorie-restricted
diabetic
fat-controlled
fat-restricted
gluten-free

protein-restricted
sodium-restricted
food lists, restricted
sodium-restricted
food value charts & tables
caloric exchanges
diabetic exchanges
protein exchanges
lunches, packed

meal plans
measurements: household/metric
menus: everyday/holiday
recipes, total: 600
servings
restaurant dining
sweeteners, artificial
youth diets

169 Schoenberg, Hazel P., R.D. GOOD HOUSEKEEPING COOKBOOK FOR CALORIE WATCHERS PLUS RECIPES FOR 7 SPECIAL DIETS. Hearst, 1971. 377 pp. index. illus. hard $6.95.
Recipe Index: Allergy; Calorie-restricted; Diabetic; Fiber-restricted; Sodium-restricted.

Associate director of the Good Housekeeping Bureau and a registered dietitian, the author has compiled an attractive and useful book that goes far beyond the limits suggested by the title. A 60-page introductory section evaluates 11 fad diets:

Air Force diet or fat pilots diet
Bananas and skim milk diet
Calories don't count (Dr. Herman Taller)
Doctor's quick weight-loss diet, or Stillman Diet (Dr. Irwin M. Stillman)
Drinking man's diet
Famous rice diet

High-carbohydrate, Low-protein diets
High-protein, Low-carbohydrate diets
Macrobiotic diet (or Zen Macrobiotic diet)
Mayo diet
Starvation diets

The section also provides information and menus for six nutritionally sound programs of weight reduction. Menus and meal planning guides follow the basic four food groups. Weight reduction advice is given for young children, children 6–12, teens, the young family, and mature adults. Following a photo-illustrated section on exercises are the eight diet recipe sections. While calorie-restricted recipes comprise the largest single collection, virtually every such recipe is adaptable to one or more of the other seven diets included in the book. Recipes are clearly identified for all possible modifications or applications, and include necessary values (for example, milligrams of sodium, diabetic exchanges) as well as the calorie count. Each of the other seven diet recipe sections opens with an introduction to basic concepts, do's and don'ts, and foods to use or avoid. Recipes in the specialized diet sections (for example, sodium-restricted, allergy) are not calorie-restricted. Each diet category is indexed separately, and the indexes include not only recipes from the specific diet sections but all appropriate ones from the calorie-restricted section as well. Individual recipes total 750, but the multiple-use feature in the calorie-restricted section results in nearly 2500 recipe applications. Thus, the whole of Schoenberg's book is greater than the sum of the parts. Recipes in any single diet are equal to the number in a full-length cookbook. Following are the diets as listed in the table of contents, number of recipes in each category, and information for each recipe in a particular category:

> Allergy: 280; egg-, gluten-, milk-, wheat-free; servings
> Bland, low-residue (fiber-restricted) and gall bladder (fat-restricted): 140; fat, total; servings
> Diabetic: 410; exchanges; servings
> High-iron: 210; iron; servings
> Low-calorie: 580; calories; servings
> Low-fat, low-cholesterol: 430; (fat-controlled) fat, total; servings
> Low-purine: 240; fat: total; servings
> Low-sodium: 200; sodium; servings

beverages, alcoholic
canning (diabetic)
convenience foods
food lists, permitted
  bland (fiber-restricted)
  low-fat, low-cholesterol
    (fat-controlled and fat-
    restricted)
  high-iron
  low-purine
  low-sodium
food lists, restricted
  bland, low-residue, low-
    fat (fiber-restricted)

low-fat, low-cholesterol
  (fat-controlled and fat-
  restricted)
low-purine
low-sodium
food value charts & tables
  calories
  carbohydrates
  fat: total
  iron
  protein
  sodium
height/weight charts

meal plans
menus: everyday
minimum daily
  requirements
recipes, total: 750
  (see above)
  diet category
  servings
recommended dietary allowances (RDA)
seasonings
sweeteners, artificial
youth diets

170 Small, Marvin. THE SPECIAL DIET COOK BOOK. Hawthorn, 1969. 544 pp. index. illus. hard $6.95.

Recipe Index: Calorie-restricted; Diabetic; Fiber-restricted; Sodium-restricted.

The author has written *The World's Best Recipes*, and originally published his *Special Diet Cook Book* in 1952. A new, revised edition appeared in 1969. Each of the seven diet sections has a short introduction on the diet's fundamentals and an illustrated list of recommended and restricted foods. While not as comprehensive as some lists in some other books, the illustrations effectively present information on sizes or portions. Calorie-restricted recipes number twice those of any other diet; the length of the other diet recipe collections is about equal. Each diet is indexed separately. Although caloric values are given with all low-sodium recipes and for many diabetic recipes, these are not included in the low-calorie index. The only menus are those for diabetics; all are evaluated in terms of both diabetic exchanges and gram weights. By means of simple bar graphs in the appendix calorie chart, the reader can quickly grasp the relative caloric values of common foods. This helpful visual presentation also contains the number of calories in the food represented. Brand name ingredients are used in many of the recipes, and brand name information is given for cereals, baking mixes, and canned soups in the low-calorie recipe section and in the appendix.

beverages, alcoholic
brand name information
food lists, permitted
   brand name information
   bland (fiber-restricted)
   high-caloric
   fat-controlled, fat-
      restricted
   high-residue
   sodium-restricted
food lists, restricted
   bland (fiber-restricted)
   fat-controlled, fat-
      restricted
   sodium-restricted

food value charts & tables
   calories
   carbohydrates
   diabetic exchanges
   fat: total
   protein
height/weight charts
menus: everyday
recipes, total: 1250
   bland (fiber-restricted):
     130; servings
   calorie, high: 110; calo-
     ries; servings

calorie-restricted: 450;
   servings
diabetic: 150; carbohy-
   drates; diabetic
   exchanges; fat: total;
   protein; servings
fat-controlled: 145;
   servings
residue, high: 150;
   servings
sodium-restricted: 115;
   calories; servings;
   sodium
seasonings

Supplementary Books

171 Krause, Marie V., M.S., R.D., and Hunscher, Martha A., M.Ed., R.D., M.R.S.H. FOOD, NUTRITION AND DIET THERAPY, 5th ed. Saunders, 1972. 718 pp. index. illus. hard $9.75.
Recipe Index: Allergy; Gluten-restricted; Phenylalanine-restricted; Protein-restricted.

The co-authors, combining expertise in dietetics and nursing, have produced a basic textbook for student nurses, public health workers, and college students in dietetics, home economics, and medicine. It is listed here because of its greater depth of background material, as well as for its hard to find information on phenylalanine-restricted diets, hypoglycemia diets, hyperlipoproteinemia diets, copper-restricted diets, and discussion of arthritis and diet. The book has three divisions: Normal Nutrition and Foods, comprising nearly half the book; Diet Therapy, which details diseases, disorders, and their dietary treatment, and which is almost as long as the first section; Foods, which concerns the basic four food groups with a sampling of recipes for each group, and the therapeutic diet recipe section, occupying only about one-tenth of the book's volume. Because nutrition and diet therapy are approached from several angles, not all of the material pertaining to a single diet is found in one place. An excellent index, however, solves this problem. Lists of food values in the 80-page appendix contain far more quantitative information than most publications.

172 Iowa State Department of Health, Nutrition Service, in cooperation with the Iowa Dietetic Assn. SIMPLIFIED DIET MANUAL WITH MEAL PATTERNS, 3rd ed. Iowa State Univ. Press, 1969. 106 pp. index. hard $4.50.

Originally designed to help nurses, cooks, and other personnel in small Iowa hospitals and nursing homes, this paragon of clarity and simplicity has gone through innumerable printings and can now be found in every state in the country. As a diet manual it contains no recipes, but lays down qualitative and quantitative guidelines for seven basic diets with some 30 modifications. Starting with a general diet grounded in the basic four food groups, it succinctly outlines each diet as to use, nutritional adequacy, and principles. Sections dealing with modifications of the major diets briefly note variations, and list foods to be used or avoided. The appendix advises on safeguards to follow in food handling, service, and storage. Reference to this book will quickly answer many questions about the why and how of modified diets. The table of contents lists the following diets and modifications:

General diet: pregnancy; lactation; older person; children; high calorie, high
  protein, high vitamin
Soft diet: bland (4 modifications); low residue (fiber-restricted)
Liquid diet: 3 modifications
Diabetic diets: 10 modifications, including fat-controlled
Calorie-restricted diets: 8 modifications
Fat-restricted diets (low-fat)
Fat-controlled and low-cholesterol diets: 2 modifications
Sodium-restricted: 5 modifications
Low purine

Brochures and Product-Related Materials

173 General Mills Chemicals. DIETETIC PAYGEL® BAKING MIX. 20 3 × 5 index cards. free.

Recipe Index: Gluten-restricted; Phenylalanine-restricted; Protein-restricted.

Set of index cards with recipes for coffee cake, English muffins, pancakes, rolls, etc., made with manufacturer's product for gluten-, phenylalanine-, and protein-restricted diets.

brand name information	carbohydrates	protein
recipes: 19	phenylalanine	servings
calories	potassium	sodium

174 General Mills Chemicals. DIETETIC PAYGEL-P® WHEAT STARCH RECIPES. 14 pp. illus. paper. free.

Recipe Index: Phenylalanine-restricted; protein-restricted.

Small recipe booklet gives information and recipes for baked goods suitable for phenylalanine- and protein-restricted diets. Breads, cookies, and puddings are the featured foods made with the manufacturer's product.

brand name information	carbohydrates	protein
recipes: 22	phenylalanine	servings
calories	potassium	sodium

175 General Mills Chemicals. MORE GOOD THINGS MADE WITH DIETETIC PAYGEL-P™ WHEAT STARCH. 27 pp. illus. paper. free.

Recipe Index: Phenylalanine-restricted; protein-restricted.

Cooking tips and recipes for main dishes and baked goods are given, using the manufacturer's product. Recipes are suitable for phenylalanine- and protein-restricted diets.

brand name information	potassium
recipes: 45	protein
calories	servings
carbohydrates	sodium
phenylalanine	references

176 General Mills Chemicals. RECIPES FOR APROTEN® LOW PROTEIN IMITATION PASTA AND PORRIDGE. 1971. 12 pp. illus. free.

Recipe Index: Gluten-restricted; Phenylalanine-restricted; Protein-restricted.

Recipes for main dishes, desserts, and salads are provided using the manufacturer's product. Recipes are appropriate for gluten-, phenylalanine-, and protein-restricted diets.

brand name information	carbohydrates	protein
recipes: 23	phenylalanine	servings
calories	potassium	sodium

K.
Diets for Special Conditions

K-1. Diets in Pregnancy and Lactation

Pregnancy and lactation call for increased amounts of protein, minerals, vitamins, and calories. Several books discuss these special needs, either in general terms or within the context of particular therapeutic diets.

For supplementary information on diets in pregnancy and/or lactation *see* Calorie-restricted diets: 13; Diabetic diets: 115, 119; Multiple diets: 171, 172; Nonprofessional nutrition education: 182, 183, 184, 185, 191, 197; Vegetarian diets: 206, 207, 208.

K-2. Youth Diets

The use of therapeutic diets for youngsters can present many problems because of their nutritional needs for growth and their parochial eating habits. Books that offer assistance in coping with these problems are listed below. A good number of books also discuss youth diets as part of good nutrition, without reference to any therapeutic diets. (The word "youth" is used broadly here, and covers the years of infancy through adolescence.)

For supplementary information on youth diets *see* Allergy diets: 1, 2, 3; Calorie-restricted diets: 13, 22, 27, 28, 29, 35, 36, 40, 46, 51; Ketogenic diets: 87, 88; Diabetic diets: 114, 115, 116, 119, 128; Gluten-restricted diets: 146, 148, 149, 151; Phenylalanine-restricted diets: 154, 155, 156; Multiple diets: 168, 169, 171, 172, 173, 175, 176; Nonprofessional nutrition education: 182, 184, 185, 186, 187, 188, 189, 191, 194, 195, 196, 197; Vegetarian diets: 206, 207.

For foreign language materials *see* Gluten-restricted diets: 152, 153.

K-3. Geriatric Diets

Reduced physical activity and a decrease in basal metabolic rate call for certain dietary changes with increasing age. A number of books discuss geriatric diets either in general terms or within the framework of specific therapeutic diets.

For supplementary information on geriatric diets *see* Allergy diets: 1; Multiple diets: 168, 169, 172; Nonprofessional nutrition education: 182, 183, 197.

II.

FOODS AND NUTRITION EDUCATION

L.

Food Composition and Values

The books in this section are general works devoted exclusively to the composition of foods, and can provide answers to food value questions related to most therapeutic diets. Books whose charts, tables, and exchange lists apply primarily to a single type of diet are collected in the appropriate diet categories.

Today's cook makes liberal use of time-saving prepared foods, such as snacks, canned soups, cake mixes, and TV dinners, so that information about basic ingredients alone is not sufficient. A list of sources of food values for familiar brand name products, which are found in other sections of this book, is printed after the annotations.

A list of all books containing exchange lists for particular diet categories follows the brand name information.

For foreign language materials *see* Protein-restricted diets: 166.

General Works

177 Bowes and Church. FOOD VALUES OF PORTIONS COMMONLY USED, 11th ed. Revised by Charles F. Church, M.D., and Helen Nichols Church. Lippincott, 1970. 180 pp. index. spiral/paper $5.40.

First published in 1937, this book is a classic reference work in the field of food values, and contains an impressive amount of information. Thousands of foods are analyzed for 26 nutrient values, and the food spectrum reaches from alligator and armadillo meat to animal crackers and TV dinners. One table lists vitamin-rich foods, and dietary supplements are included. All nutrients shown in the food value tables are defined in a glossary. Many brand name products are included, although some can be identified by brand name only by carefully checking the footnotes. The tables are arranged in food groups, such as dairy products, desserts, eggs, fruit, etc., and a fine index assists in locating specific entries. The format of the tables, using alternating light and dark horizontal bands, makes it easy to read correct values across the entire page. The book also contains tables of hundreds of non-nutritive ingredients sometimes added to processed foods; information includes the function (for example, emulsifier, flavor, color, preservative), important uses in foods, and the level of use. The minimum daily requirements for essential nutrients are given.

beverages, alcoholic	food value charts & tables	calories
bibliography	amino acids: 8	carbohydrates
convenience foods	brand name products	fat: total; polyunsaturated

food value charts (cont.)
  iron
  magnesium
  phosphorous
  potassium

protein
sodium
vitamins: 6
glossary

height/weight charts
recommended dietary allowances (RDA)
references

178 Watt, Bernice K., and Merrill, Annabel L. COMPOSITION OF FOODS: RAW, PROCESSED, PREPARED. U.S. Dept. of Agriculture, Handbook No. 8., 1963, 190 pp. paper $2.85.

This is the source book of food values from which so many other books and pamphlets have sprung. The main tables of fat, protein, carbohydrate, and calorie values contain 2480 entries, and are given twice: for the edible portion of 100 grams of food and for the edible portion of one pound of food as purchased. Each entry is numbered. Selected items are further analyzed for fatty acids, cholesterol, and magnesium, and are cross-referenced to the main tables. A useful appendix feature is a list of the common and scientific names of animals and plants included in the tables. Explanations of the food values represented are far more comprehensive and technical than those found in *Nutritive Value of Foods* (entry 179).

beverages, alcoholic
convenience foods
food value charts & tables
  calcium
  calories
  carbohydrates

cholesterol
fat: total; monounsatu-
  rated (oleic); polyun-
  saturated (linoleic);
  saturated
iron

magnesium
phosphorous
potassium
protein
sodium
vitamins (5)
water

179 U.S. Dept. of Agriculture. NUTRITIVE VALUE OF FOODS. Home and Garden Bulletin No. 72., 1971. 41 pp. paper $.85.

A standard government publication of food values, this includes 600 numbered entries. Information is presented in a simple, nontechnical style. Measurements used in the tables are explained, and there is a practical review of the recommended daily dietary allowances.

beverages, alcoholic
bibliography
convenience foods
food value charts & tables
  calcium

calories
carbohydrates
fat: total; monounsatu-
  rated (oleic); polyun-
  saturated (linoleic);
  saturated

iron
vitamins
recommended dietary allowances (RDA)
references

180 Maryland Dietetic Assn. NUTRITIONAL ANALYSIS OF SELECTED COMMERCIAL PRODUCTS. 1973. 25 pp. paper $1.30 postpaid.

This useful booklet shows the nutritional value for several hundred brand name convenience foods, including canned fish, cereals, desserts, entrées, frozen breakfasts, instant foods, juices, salad dressings, sauces, snacks, soups, textured vegetable protein products, and TV dinners.

convenience foods
food value charts & tables
  brand name products
  calories

carbohydrates
fat: total
iron

potassium
protein
sodium

181 Szanton, Jules G. FOOD VALUES AND CALORIE CHARTS. Frederick Fell, 1965. 153 pp. index. hard. $5.95.

A handy reference work compiled by a man formerly in charge of new product development for a dietetic food company, this title contains a great deal of useful information on more than 2000 foods. The substantial introduction discusses the role of nutrients in good health. The remainder of the book is divided into three sections. Section 1 gives the caloric value of both brand name products and unprocessed foods. The protein, fat, and carbohydrate values for food portions, however, are stated as percentages of the composition rather than in grams, as is the standard practice. Thus, the reader will have to make mathematical calculations before using the information in a therapeutic diet. In Section 2 much the same list of foods is repeated, but values for vitamins are given (in milligrams). Section 3 combines several features. Calorie-restricted foods, such as cookies and salad dressings, are analyzed as in Section 1 for calories, protein, fat, and carbohydrate (percentage composition). A long chart covers the sodium and potassium content of foods (milligrams). A list somewhat shorter than the others is devoted to the fatty acid content of typical foods, but does not include brand name products. An allergy section groups together brand name products that are citrus-, egg-, milk-, or wheat-free; there is also a list of food families. Genuinely helpful is a list of brand names with the parent company and address, and a better than average conversion table for household to metric measurements.

allergy information
bibliography
brand name information
convenience foods
food value charts & tables
  calories
  carbohydrates (%)

fat: total (%); monoun-
  saturated (oleic); polyunsaturated (linoleic);
  saturated
potassium
protein (%)

sodium
vitamins/minerals
height/weight charts
measurements: metric/
  'household
recommended dietary allowances (RDA)

Brand Names

For food composition values of brand name products *see:*

Calorie-restricted diets: 29
Fat-controlled diets: 62, 75, 81
Ketogenic diets: 87
Sodium-restricted diets: 93, 99
Diabetic diets: 105, 110,111, 112, 113, 114, 115, 122, 125, 127, 128, 134, 135
Gluten-restricted diets: 145, 148, 150
Phenylalanine-restricted diets: 154
Protein-restricted diets: 157, 160, 161, 165
Multiple diets: 170
Food composition and values: 177, 180, 181
Vegetarian diets: 209

Exchange Lists

For diet categories whose books contain exchange lists *see:*

Caloric: 12, 16, 20, 22, 26, 28, 30, 31, 35, 37, 38, 45, 50, 69, 168, 207
Cholesterol-lowering: 67

M.
Evaluation of Popular Diets

Diets promoting nirvana through nutrition or instantaneous weight loss are never in short supply. Many popular diets are deficient in important nutrients, and some such diets can cause real physical harm. Nonetheless, fad diets will be an indestructible force so long as they promise "something for nothing," a lure that never fails to attract.

Some fad diets fade from the scene, but many others reappear every few years under new names. Others are passed along by word-of-mouth, and thus survive long after the mass media have lost interest in them.

Several books discuss and evaluate a score of well-known diets. These evaluations, although in scattered locations, provide an excellent means for checking on the nutritional soundness of popular diets. Furthermore, they offer good guidelines for making sensible judgments on "new" diets.

For information on popular diets *see* Calorie-restricted diets: 40, 46; Multiple diets: 169, 171; Nonprofessional nutrition education: 190; Vegetarian diets: 206.

N.
Nonprofessional Nutrition Education

Books

182 Deutsch, Ronald M. THE FAMILY GUIDE TO BETTER FOOD AND BETTER HEALTH. Meredith, 1971. 277 pp. index. illus. hard $7.95; Bantam. paper $1.95.

The author has written numerous articles and books on nutrition and health sciences, and is a frequent speaker before professional nutrition and medical audiences. His book is enthusiastically recommended by the major nutrition journals. According to the foreword, written by Dr. Philip L. White, director, Department of Foods and Nutrition, American Medical Association, and which has been quoted by the *Journal of Nutrition Education* (Fall 1971, p. 79), Deutsch's book is a "... totally acceptable, comprehensive book on nutrition for the layman." Although the author delves far deeper into the basic concepts of body chemistry and nutrition than any other book listed in this work, the information is always fascinating and readily understandable.

The seven main sections of the book, in addition to lists of recommended and nonrecommended reading, are "Your Food and Your Health," "How Food Becomes Life" (transformation of carbohydrate, fat, and protein into living tissue), "The Nutritionist on the Scales" (weight loss), "The Nutritionist in the Supermarket" (processed foods, labels, pesticides), "The Food Scientist in the Kitchen" (food handling, storage, and utilization), "The Doctor Looks at Eating and Illness" (digestion, indigestion, heart disease), and "Food, Growth and Aging" (pregnant and lactating women, children, older adults). The illustrations, question-and-answer sections, and index are all very helpful.

bibliography	carbohydrates	height/weight charts
convenience foods	fat: total	recommended dietary allow-
food value charts & tables	protein	ances (RDA)
calories	vitamins/minerals	youth diets

183 Leverton, Ruth M., Ph.D. FOOD BECOMES YOU, 3rd ed. Iowa State Univ. Press, 1965. 208 pp. index. illus. hard $5.50.

The author, who holds a doctorate in nutrition and who has written many practical books on nutrition, is the assistant administrator of the Agricultural Research

Service of the U.S. Department of Agriculture. First published in 1952, her book has earned a high reputation among dietitians as a good, all-round explanation of nutrition for the lay person. Leverton deals with nutrition on a far more elementary level than Deutsch's book (entry 182), and is suitable for the person who is willing to accept the author's word on her reputation. Deutsch's book, on the other hand, is filled with case histories and references to scientific studies; it presumes a certain skepticism on the part of readers, and challenges them to absorb and master a highly complex subject. The content of Leverton's simpler book is more directly related to eating patterns. She discusses overweight (listing a week's menus for 1200 and 1600 calorie diets), children, teenagers, older adults, and pregnant and lactating women. The often-neglected underweight person is provided helpful information. The basic four food groups, food fads, and the relationship of physical activity and caloric requirements are all covered.

beverages, alcoholic	fat: total	menus: everyday
convenience foods	protein	recommended dietary allow-
food value charts & tables	vitamins/minerals	ances (RDA)
calories	height/weight charts	youth diets
carbohydrates	meal plans	

184 White, Philip L., Sc.D. LET'S TALK ABOUT FOOD. American Medical Assn., 1970. 198 pp. index. illus. paper $2.

The author is director, Department of Foods and Nutrition of the American Medical Association. With the addition of some topics of current interest, material in this book has been extracted from a column of the same name from the AMA's magazine *Today's Health*. The range of information is broad and fascinating. Typical questions are: "Is food from vending machines safe?" "How does low sodium milk compare in nutritive value with regular milk?" "Are the terms 'starch' and 'carbohydrate' synonymous?" "What are acid and alkaline foods, and should they be balanced in the diet?" "Do raw orange peels contain something harmful?" The author seems to have uncovered a great many questions that people may have been hesitant to ask or have not known how to verbalize. The material is grouped into chapters, and a good index permits the reader to check any subject quickly. Besides the normal coverage of nutrients, weight control, and modifications of the diet, major subjects are commercially prepared foods and the use of food additives.

beverages, alcoholic	sweeteners, artificial
convenience foods	youth diets

185 Crocker, Betty. HOW TO FEED YOUR FAMILY TO KEEP THEM FIT & HAPPY, NO MATTER WHAT. Golden Press, 1972. 159 pp. index. illus. paper $1.50.

While it is uncertain whether or not Betty Crocker really exists, the validity of this book is attested to by Dr. William H. Sebrell, Jr., former director of the Institute of Nutrition Sciences, Columbia University. Using the basic four food groups as the foundation, the book gives practical advice on weight loss, fat-controlled diets, and diet during pregnancy. Its advantage over other titles is its recognition of certain problems that most nutrition authors ignore because they are not supposed to happen. Some examples include children who hate vegetables, people who refuse to sit down and eat a sensible breakfast, sick people who must be enticed to eat, parents yearning

for spicy or gourmet food while their children refuse to venture beyond total bland-
ness, the presence of a health food fan in the house, and small children who stuff themselves with sweets at birthday parties. Each situation is evaluated in terms of whether
or not it represents a nutritional disaster, and, if so, what to do about it. A chart of
the most commonly used food additives is included. The recipes back up some of the
problem areas of eating: unorthodox but delicious suggestions for the recalcitrant
breakfast eater, a sampling of fat-controlled recipes, and the usual tribute to low-
calorie dishes.

food value charts & tables	meal plans	calories
calories	menus: everyday	servings
height/weight charts	recipes: 70	seasonings
lunches, packed		youth diets

186 McWilliams, Margaret, and Davis, Linda. FOOD FOR YOU. Ginn, 1971. 183
pp. index. illus. paper $3.95.

This is a high school textbook on nutrition that presents the subject to teenagers
in a way related to them personally. Although some material obviously is geared
only to adolescents in a high school milieu (for example, complexion problems), the
book can be recommended to adults who wish something on a technical level halfway
between the Deutsch (entry 182) and the Leverton (entry 183) titles. Overweight,
underweight, breakfast, snacks, digestion, and assimilation are covered. A separate
chapter deals with regional differences in foods, and the nutritional worth of such
popular specialties as tacos, jambalaya, and clam chowder. A study review guide
follows each chapter.

food value charts & tables	rated (oleic); polyun-	protein
calories	saturated (linoleic);	vitamins/minerals
fat: total; monounsatu-	saturated	height/weight charts
		youth diets

Brochures and Product-Related Materials

187 National Dairy Council. A BOY AND HIS PHYSIQUE. 1970. 29 pp. illus. paper
$.30.

A book that motivates boys to develop sound nutritional habits while building
their physiques, it is closely patterned after the popular *A Girl and Her Figure* (entry
188), and was written by a professor of physical education and health, Walter H.
Gregg, Ed.D.

food value charts & tables	height/weight charts
calories	meal plans
protein	youth diets

188 National Dairy Council. A GIRL AND HER FIGURE. 1970. 25 pp. illus. paper
$.30.

A Sensible, readily understood guide to nutrition for teenage girls, this booklet
was written by a well-known nutritionist, Ruth M. Leverton, Ph.D.

food value charts & tables	height/weight charts
calories	meal plans
protein	youth diets

189 National Dairy Council. A GIRL AND HER FIGURE AND YOU. 1970. 16 pp. illus. paper $.25.

This attractive booklet, designed to accompany entry 188, encourages the practical application of good eating habits by providing write-in charts for the individual and enticing ideas for snacks.

height/weight charts
meal plans

menus: everyday
recipes: 20

190 Los Angeles District, Califonia Dietetic Assn. A DOZEN DIETS FOR BETTER OR FOR WORSE. 1973. 25 pp. paper $2.

Five dietitians and a professor of nutrition are responsible for this evaluation for consumers of popular weight reduction diets, plus a few other well-known diets designed to correct endocrine disorders or to induce a desirable spiritual state. Its scientific method, clear and concise presentation of conclusions, and willingness to make unequivocal judgments on the nutritional soundness of some of the most famous diets in the nation mark it as a book whose value is belied by its modest size.

All 12 diets are evaluated on the same criteria: the basic four food groups as provided in each diet compared with the amounts recommended by the USDA and the recommended daily dietary allowances for nutrients (RDA) supplied by the diet as compared with guidelines set up by the Food and Nutrition Board, National Academy of Sciences. The authors chose a 22- to 35-year-old woman's RDA as the base for comparison because adult women are most often concerned with dieting. The critique of each diet includes a summary statement interpreting the results of a nutritional analysis and a recommendation as to the diet's acceptability. A chart illustrates conformance of the diet to the minimum number of servings of the basic four food groups; diets are marked "OK" or are given a numerical rating. The RDA evaluation on the chart is done on a percentage basis. Menus on which each diet was evaluated are displayed next to the charts and summaries. The diets evaluated are:

> Diet for endocrine disorders, Henry G. Bieler
> Diet revolution, Robert C. Atkins
> Diet watchers guide, Ann Gold and Sara Briller
> Knox eat and reduce plan, Knox Gelatin Company
> Low carbohydrate diet (Air Force diet), Bonomo Culture Institute
> Simeons diet, Harold Harper
> Skim milk and bananas diet, Irwin Stillman
> Dr. Stillman's quick weight loss beauty diet, Irwin Stillman and Samm Baker
> Ten day, ten pounds off diet, Ernestine Carter
> Three week 555 diet (Doctors quick weight loss diet), Irwin Stillman
> Weight watchers diet, Weight Watchers International
> Zen macrobiotic diet, Georges Ohsawa

recommended dietary allow-
    ances (RDA)

references

191 U.S. Dept. of HEW. FACTS ABOUT NUTRITION. DHEW Publ. No. (NIH) 74-423. 1973. 28 pp. illus. paper $.35.

In relatively simple language this brochure explains the basic four food groups, and nutritional requirements for adults, teenagers, pregnant and lactating women, infants, and those trying to lose or gain weight.

height/weight charts   references
meal plans   youth diets
menus: everyday

192 U.S. Dept. of HEW. WE WANT YOU TO KNOW ABOUT LABELS ON
    FOODS. DHEW Publ. No. (FDA) 73-2043. 1973. single page. illus. $.25.

    How to read and interpret information on food labels is the subject of this folder,
which supplements entry 193.

convenience foods

193 U.S. Dept. of HEW. WE WANT YOU TO KNOW WHAT WE KNOW ABOUT
    NUTRITION LABELS ON FOOD. DHEW Publ. No. (FDA) 73-2039. 1973.
    single page. illus. $.20.

    This folder explains how to read the new nutrition labels that are now appearing
on all fortified foods and foods for which a nutrition claim is made.

convenience foods
recommended dietary allow-
    ances (RDA)

194 American Medical Assn. CAN FOOD MAKE THE DIFFERENCE? 1964.
    single page. illus. paper $.15.

    Folder advises teenagers on good nutrition, weight loss, and the basic four food
groups.

youth diets

195 American Medical Assn. YOUR AGE & YOUR DIET: INFANCY THROUGH
    ADULTHOOD. 1971. 9 pp. illus. paper $.10.

    Booklet offers tips for all members of the family, using the basic four food groups
as the foundation for good nutrition.

youth diets

196 Nutrition Foundation. FOOD CHOICES: THE TEEN-AGE GIRL. 1966. 11
    pp. paper. single copy free.

    Basic nutrition for young women is explained as an exercise in freedom and re-
sponsibility in making wise choices about food. Fortunately, the introductory theme,
which portrays young women as filled with empty-headed concerns about hair and
makeup, never gets beyond page 1.

youth diets

197 Nutrition Foundation. FOOD: A KEY TO BETTER HEALTH. 21 pp. illus.
    paper $.30.

    The simplest and most colorful of the Nutrition Foundation booklets, this one
illustrates not only the basic four food groups but also the sources for key nutrients.
Short chapters deal with weight control, pregnancy, youngsters, teenagers, and older
adults.

menus: everyday   youth diets

198 Nutrition Foundation. YOUR DIET: HEALTH IS IN THE BALANCE. 1966. 22 pp. paper. single copy free.

This basic program for good nutrition covers weight control, fat control, and the need for iron and fiber in the diet.

bibliography   height/weight charts   meal plans

O.
Vegetarian Diets

The vegetarian diets presented in this section are normal diets. They are unconventional chiefly because they forgo the use of meat, poultry, and fish. Plant proteins, however, are different from animal proteins, so that certain steps must be taken to assure nutritional adequacy in vegetarian diets. "Lacto-ovo" vegetarian diets include eggs, milk, cheese, and similar secondary animal products. "Vegan," or pure vegetarian diets, exclude *all* animal products, and cannot supply all essential nutrients without some dietary supplements. Most books annotated in this section advise the reader of these important facts.

For additional information on the use of textured protein (TVP) products, or meat analogs *see* Diabetic diets: 112; Food composition and values: 180.

Cookbooks

For additional vegetarian recipes *see* Calorie-restricted diets: 47; Fat-controlled diets: 61, 68; Diabetic diets: 135.

199 Lappé, Frances Moore. DIET FOR A SMALL PLANET. Ballantine, 1971. 301 pp. index. illus. paper $1.25.

Much more than a routine vegetarian cookbook, nearly half of Lappé's work is concerned with the prospect of providing ample protein for the world's population. She maintains that scarce world agricultural resources are largely devoted to the production of animal protein, and that this is far less efficient than the direct production and consumption of plant protein. Both the Chicago Nutrition Association (*Nutrition References and Book Reviews*, p. 20, 1972) and the *Journal of Nutrition Education* (Spring 1972, p. 79) reviewers acknowledge the author's understanding of the latest concepts of protein theory: incomplete plant proteins must be combined to provide the necessary balance of essential amino acids in the diet, and all essential amino acids must be consumed at the same time in order to be utilized. Excellent charts and graphs explain these concepts; the menus and recipes follow through on the practical application of "protein complementarity." In a special editorial note introducing its review, however, the *Journal of Nutrition Education* cautions: "It should not be considered a complete nutrition text." The recipes, filling the second half of the book, are anything but the bowl of gruel type often associated with this type of cookery. Rather, they are a good balance between international dishes—

94

Chinese, Indian, Italian, Japanese, and Mexican—and unmistakably American foods, such as Indian pudding, peanut butter logs, and Boston brown bread. Each recipe notes the percentage of the daily protein allowance provided, as well as the usable grams of protein in an average serving. Appendix tables give the cost per usable gram of protein for dairy products, legumes, grains and cereals, seafoods, nuts and seeds, and meat and poultry.

food value charts & tables	recipes: 110
protein	protein
vitamins/minerals	servings
menus: everday	references

Black, Patricia Hall, M.S., and Carey, Ruth Little, Ph.D. VEGETARIAN COOKERY. 5 vols. Pacific Press, 1971. index. illus. hard/spiral $3.50 each; $15.95 complete set.

This five-volume series (*see* entries 200–204) of cookbooks has in common an easy to follow format, appetizing recipe collections, and the most exhaustive nutritional analysis of recipes offered in any of the cookbooks considered in this work. Each sturdy and attractive volume provides an excellent variety of recipes for the lacto-ovo vegetarian diet. Many recipes call for brand name textured vegetable protein (TVP) products. Two versions of the same recipe often are given—with or without eggs—so that more options are offered to strict vegetarians. The series' unique feature is the computer-calculated nutritional analysis for 17 factors in each recipe, with calories and quantities of nutrients listed for the total recipe and for a single serving in extensive tables in the appendix.

200 VEGETARIAN COOKERY 1: APPETIZERS, SALADS, BEVERAGES. 96 pp.

Also includes dressings and relishes. Special features on equivalents (amount purchased: cooked yield) for fruits and vegetables. 190 recipes.

201 VEGETARIAN COOKERY 2: BREADS, SOUPS, SANDWICHES. 93 pp.

Also includes sauces and gravies, information on puréeing vegetables. 180 recipes.

202 VEGETARIAN COOKERY 3: MAIN DISHES, VEGETABLES. 126 pp.

Comprehensive chart of cooking methods for a large number of vegetables. 160 recipes.

203 VEGETARIAN COOKERY 4: PIES, CAKES, COOKIES, DESSERTS. 126 pp.

Includes equivalent measures, substitutions for common baking ingredients. 250 recipes.

204 VEGETARIAN COOKERY 5: EXOTIC FOODS, CANDIES, COOKING FOR A CROWD. 96 pp.

Most recipes in quantity cookery section yield 24 or 50 servings, with some as high as 70 servings. Scope includes beverages, pastry, salads, soups, vegetables, desserts, and sandwiches. Candies and "exotic foods" (mostly Brazilian, Chinese, Japanese, Korean, Mexican, and Filipino) yield enough for a family. 180 recipes.

brand name information	fat: total; monounsatu-	protein
lunches, packed	rated (oleic); polyun-	servings
recipes: 960 total	saturated (linoleic);	sodium
calories	saturated	vitamins/minerals
carbohydrates	potassium	references

205 Ewald, Ellen Buchman. RECIPES FOR A SMALL PLANET. Ballantine, 1973. 367 pp. index. illus. paper $1.50.

Both a precursor and a successor to its acknowledged relative, Lappé's *Diet for a Small Planet* (entry 199), this title has a curious history. The author first introduced Frances Lappé to vegetarian cookery. Ms. Lappé then investigated the rationale for proper vegetarian nutrition (protein complementarity), and published an exposition of the subject in a popular cookbook, *Diet for a Small Planet*. Having learned from her friend as they worked together on some of the recipes, Ms. Ewald began to apply the protein complementarity concept in her own kitchen. She revised old favorites among her own recipes (which had originally gained Ms. Lappé's interest) and created new ones; the result is the present book. Almost one-quarter of the book is devoted to practical aspects of this type of cooking: an explanation of protein complementarity and how to apply it, several pages on food for camping, tips on enriching the protein value of standard recipes, yogurt making, helpful kitchen equipment (with or without electricity), and a useful glossary. The appealing recipes include a real variety—from granola and bean Stroganoff to Thanksgiving cranberry bread. Indicated on each recipe are the grams of usable protein and the percent of average daily protein need, as well as the protein ingredients in terms of their complementarity (relative amounts of different types of protein that combine to give maximum protein utilization).

food value charts & tables	freezing	recipes: 280
calories	glossary	protein
protein	lunches, packed	servings
		references

General Works

For additional supplementary information on vegetarian diets *see* Multiple diets: 169, 171.

206 Marsh, Alice G., M.S., R.D.; Christensen, Dorothy, M.S., R.D.; Stoia, Rose G., R.D.; Fagal, Sylvia M., M.S., R.D.; and Schmitz, Darlene R., R.D. ABOUT NUTRITION. Southern Publishing Assn., 1971. 187 pp. illus. paper $2.95.

Six registered dietitians from the Seventh-day Adventist Dietetic Association collaborated in writing this interesting, highly readable book about good nutrition that incorporates a lacto-ovo vegetarian diet. The book makes no claims or apologies for such a diet; the outlook is that of the professional nutritionist, not a religious or philosophical advocate. The scope is broad enough to encompass a fairly technical explanation of metabolism as well as practical suggestions for implementing nutritionally sound, tasty diets for every individual. Particularly good features concern food quackery and a month's suggestions for packed lunches. The recommended reading list is extensive. Unfortunately, the book has no index.

| bibliography | food value charts & tables | fat: total; monounsatu- |
| entertaining | calcium | rated (oleic); polyun- |

saturated (linoleic);
saturated
protein
vitamins/minerals
lunches, packed

meal plans
menus: everyday
references
youth diets

207 Carey, Ruth Little, Ph.D.; Vyhmeister, Irma Bachmann, M.S.; and Hudson, Jennie Stagg, M.A. COMMONSENSE NUTRITION. Pacific Press, 1971. 166 pp. index. paper $2.95.

Prepared by the School of Nutrition and Dietetics of Loma Linda University as a science nutrition source book, this work covers much of the same ground as *About Nutrition* (entry 206), but with more emphasis on kitchen applications. As in the Seventh-day Adventist book, the authors discuss only nutrition, and don't venture into reasons why individuals may choose this type of diet. Meal plans and menus are provided throughout the book, and the introduction notes that recipes for most of the entrées and special dishes can be found in the *Vegetarian Cookery* series (*see* entries 200–204). A whole chapter is devoted to budget cookery and another to packed lunches. Sodium-restricted, fat-controlled, and calorie-restricted diet information is included. The list of caloric exchanges incorporates brand name vegetarian products.

brand name information
food lists
  permitted
  restricted
food value charts & tables

brand name products
caloric exchanges
height/weight charts
lunches, packed
meal plans

menus: everyday
recommended dietary allowances (RDA)
references
youth diets

208 Seventh-day Adventist Dietetic Assn. IT'S YOUR WORLD OF GOOD FOOD: COOKING FOR HEALTH & HAPPINESS. 2 vol. Voice of Prophecy. 48 pp. each. illus. paper $1 for set.

Designed to teach good nutrition within the framework of a vegetarian diet, these two volumes make an attractive and interesting set. Each contains six chapters that are followed by short quizzes on the material learned, and several recipes. The first volume introduces the basic four food groups, vitamins, and minerals. The second book concerns application: meal planning, cooking tips, needs of pregnant and lactating women, snacks, weight reduction, cutting the cost of food, the rationale for a vegetarian diet, and a better than average section on packed lunches. Meal plans are given for both lacto-ovo and pure vegetarian diets. Some brand name information is given in the footnotes. The concept of protein complementarity, however, is not explained clearly.

lunches, packed
meal plans

recipes: 75
servings

references

209 Sonnenberg, Lydia, M.A., R.D.; Zolber, Kathleen, Ph.D., R.D.; and Register, U. D., Ph.D., R.D. THE VEGETARIAN DIET: FOOD FOR US ALL. American Dietetic Assn. 124 pp. loose-leaf binder $15.

Designed as a study kit to provide credit for 10 continuing education hours for registered dietitians, this book should satisfy the lay person with a deep interest in vegetarianism or the skeptic who seeks unequivocal answers to the many questions raised by the subject. Documentation is provided by countless references and six re-prints from the *Journal of the American Dietetic Association, Journal of Clinical Nutrition, Journal of the American Medical Association*, and the U.S. Department of Agriculture. Topics covered in the book include nutritional adequacy, experiences with vegetarian dietaries in large populations, historical background, religious and philosophical motives of vegetarians, economics, comparison of flesh and nonflesh dietaries in different countries, and the outlook for meeting the world's future protein requirements. Practical aspects encompass abundant information on brand name textured vegetable protein products, a week's menus for both lacto-ovo and pure vegetarians, shopping hints for nutrition and economy, and cost comparisons of meat and textured vegetable protein counterparts. All recipes are for entrées; the cost per serving is given. A pre-examination surveys the reader's knowledge at the beginning of the book and a more complete test is given at the end. In all, it is a substantial ex-position that should be valuable to the more advanced and inquisitive reader.

bibliography	fat: total; monounsatu-	recipes: 16
brand name information	rated (oleic); polyun-	calories
convenience foods	saturated (linoleic);	carbohydrates
food value charts & tables	unsaturated; saturated	fat: total
amino acids	potassium	potassium
brand names	protein	protein
calcium	sodium	servings
calories	vitamins/minerals	recommended dietary allow-
carbohydrates	menus: everyday	ances (RDA)
		references

210 Zolber, Kathleen, Ph.D., R.D., and Register, U. D., Ph.D., R.D. VEGETARI-ANISM. American Dietetic Assn. 60-min tape cassette with study guide $6.

Two experts on vegetarian nutrition cover the most important aspects of the subject in a question-and-answer format. Favorable reaction to this tape by dietitians (it is worth two continuing education hours) spurred development of the more compre-hensive treatment of the subject given in entry 209, *Vegetarianism: Food for Us All.* After an introduction to the historical roots of vegetarianism, Zolber and Register touch upon world food production and present-day interest in vegetarians among such groups as young persons, the counterculture, religious groups, and "middle Americans" on budgets. A high level of technical understanding is necessary to ap-preciate every part of the discussion on protein nutrition, but examples and guidelines should be clear to the intelligent listener. The composition of textured vegetable protein meat analogs is covered, as well as the shortcomings of Zen macrobiotic diets and the success of different vegetarian dietaries followed either voluntarily or because of wartime meat shortages. Numerous studies are cited throughout the tape as sup-porting evidence. Of interest to the person on a fat-controlled diet is the information on the effects of vegetarian diets on serum cholesterol and the incidence of heart disease.

211 Register, U. D., Ph.D., R.D., and Sonnenberg, L. M., R.D. THE VEGETAR-IAN DIET. American Dietetic Assn., 1973. 9 pp. paper $.80.

This reprint from the *Journal of the American Dietetic Association* takes into account both scientific and practical considerations for a vegetarian diet that provides all essential nutrients. Presented on a technical level, it discusses adequate and inadequate vegetarian diets, citing studies of such population groups as Hunza, Lebanese, and Okinawans. Important points for fulfilling the requirements of the basic four food groups are given. The same reprint is included in entry 209, *Vegetarianism: Food for Us All.*

menus
references

III.
RECIPE INDEXES

Allergy Recipe Index

Books indexed are: 1, 2, 3, 4, 5, 6, 7, 8, 9, 10, 11, 58, 169*, 171. Allergy recipes are grouped by category in the 11 different indexes listed below. Four of these indexes contain gluten-restricted recipes, and additional recipes for this type of ingredient control are given in the separate Gluten-restricted recipe index. (For guidelines on using gluten-restricted recipes for wheat-free allergy diets *see* Part I-A, Allergy Diets.)

1. Egg-free recipes
2. Egg-, gluten-, milk-, and wheat-free recipes
3. Egg-, gluten-, and wheat-free recipes
4. Egg- and milk-free recipes
5. Egg-, milk-, and wheat-free recipes
6. Egg- and wheat-free recipes
7. Gluten-, milk-, and wheat-free recipes
8. Gluten- and wheat-free recipes
9. Milk-free recipes
10. Milk- and wheat-free recipes
11. Wheat-free recipes

Index 1: Egg-Free Recipes

Books indexed are: 3, 4, 5, 7, 8, 10, 169, 171. *See also* Allergy Recipe Indexes 2, 3, 4, 5, 6.

*In 169, some allergy recipes are not listed in the "Allergy Recipe Index," but in the "Low Calorie Recipe Index"; each such allergy recipe has been identified here by an asterisk (*).

Index 2: Egg-, Gluten-, Milk-, and Wheat-Free Recipes

Books indexed are: 3, 5, 8, 169.*

*In 169, some allergy recipes are not listed in the "Allergy Recipe Index," but in the "Low Calorie Recipe Index"; each such allergy recipe has been identified here by an asterisk (*).

Index 3: Egg-, Gluten-, and Wheat-Free Recipes

Books indexed are: 3, 5, 8, 169.* *See also* Allergy Recipe Index 2.

Appetizer, celery, sesame topped
    stuffed, 169
Apple bake, Indian, 8
Artichoke hearts with Roquefort, 5
Bars, apricot tangy, 8, *see also* Cookies
Beef, boiled, with dill, 8
Beverages
  café au crème, 169
  orange floats, 169*
Biscuits, cheese, 3
Blancmange, 3
    chocolate, 3
Bread, corn, 5
Buttermilk, blushing, 169
Cake
  apricot baba, 5
  chocolate cream refrigerator, varia-
      tions, 5
  lemon cream, 5
  orange cream, 5
  strawberry cream, variations, 5
  wine cream, 5
Carrots, cheese topped, 169
Celery, creamed, 169
Cheesecake
  lemon, 5
  orange yogurt, 5
Chicken
  curried, kabobs, 169
  curry, in a hurry, 169
  Henny Penny, 3
  pie, 3
Cookies *see also* Bars
  almond rolls, lacy, 8
  butter nut, no bake, 3
  caramel crunch, 3
  coconut chewies, 3
  cream cheese, marmalade topped, 8
  peanut caramel crunch, 3
Dessert
  frozen
      lemon crème, Millicent's, 169

Dessert, frozen (cont.)
    rainbow whip, 169
    strawberry frost, 169
  Persian rice, 169
  salad, cottage cheese, 169
Fish, baked, with horseradish sauce, 169
Floating island, rice, 3
Flounder, mambo, 169
Fruit
  ambrosia tropicale, 169
  compote
      Iranian pineapple, 169*
      our favorite, 169
Gelatin, orange bagatelle, 8
Ham pie, 3
Ice cream
  grape, 169
  lemon, 5
  pink mint, 169
  strawberry, elegant, 5
  variations, 5
Linguine Alfredo, dieter's, 169*
Liver, beef, onions au fromage, 169
Meat balls, porcupine, 8
Milk shake, pineapple banana, 169
Mousse
  apricot rum, variations, 5
  berry mallow, 5
  burnt almond, 5
  chocolate, 5
      peppermint, 5
  orange marshmallow cream, 5
  peppermint, 5
  pineapple and peppermint, 5
Muffins, corn sticks, 3
Pancakes
  corn cakes, crusty, 5
  potato soybean, 3
Parfait
  cherry banana festival, 169
  raspberry, 169
  royale, 169

*In 169, some allergy recipes are not listed in the "Allergy Recipe Index," but in the "Low Calorie Recipe Index"; each such allergy recipe has been identified here by an asterisk (*).

Pie
  cream, 3
  fruit, 3
  ice cream, chocolate, 5
Potatoes
  baked, Swedish, 5
  creamed, Tacy's, 8, 169
  rebaked, 169
Pudding
  blushing bride, 8
  rhubarb, 169
    whip, 169
  rice
    blueberry, 169
    cinnamon, 3
    raisin, 3
Salad
  Cajik, 169
  cheese
    garden, 169
    petal, 169
  dilly cukes, 169
  green, blushing, 169
  peach, 169
Salad dressing
  cheese, tangy, 169
  dilled cottage cheese, 169
  horseradish herb, 8, 169
  mayonnaise, 3, 8
  Russian, 8

Salad dressing (cont.)
  sour cream, 3
  yogurt, 169
Sauce
  curry, 169
  lemon, 3
  white, 8
Scallops en brochette, 169
Sherbet
  apricot buttermilk, 5
  apricot milk, variations, 5
  array, 169
  berry, 5
  blueberry festive parfait, 169
  cranberry, 5
  lemon, 5
    orange, 5
  lemon cups, 169
  orange, 5
  pineapple, homemade, 169
  pineapple buttermilk, 5
  three fruit, 5
Sole
  à la Parisienne, 169
  baked, chervil, 169
Spinach, gourmet style, 169
Strawberries, in almond yogurt, 169
Topping, whipped milk, 5
Tuna pie, 3
Waffles, potato soybean, 3
Zucchini Parmigiana, 169

Index 4: Egg- and Milk-Free Recipes

Books indexed are: 3, 4, 5, 7, 8, 9, 10, 11, 169. *See also* Allergy Recipe Indexes 2, 5.

Bars *see also* Cookies
  butterscotch, 4
  coffee raisin, 4
  cranberry coconut, 5
  filled
    apricot, 4
    coconut date, 4
  fruit squares, frosted, 4
  oatmeal toffee, 4
  peanut butter, 4
Beef, Madeira, in rice ring, 10
Biscuits, 9
Bread
  Annette's, 5

Bread (cont.)
  banana, 5
    tea, 8
  batter, basic, 9
  date, 5
  oatmeal, 3
    molasses, 9
  orange, 5
  pumpkin, 3
  refrigerator, 9
  sourdough, French, 5
  white, 3, 11
Brownies, 4
Buta Manju, 5

Index 5: Egg-, Milk-, and Wheat-Free Recipes

Books indexed are: 1, 3, 6, 7, 8, 9, 10, 11, 58, 169, 171. *See also* Allergy Recipe Index 2.

Vegetables
  in casserole, 1
  combinations, 1
Waffles, 1
  buckwheat yeast, 1

Whitefish, steamed, 1
Yams, baked, 1
Zucchini, 1
  baked stuffed, 1

Index 6: Egg- and Wheat-Free Recipes

Books indexed are: 3, 6, 7, 8, 10, 169, 171. *See also* Allergy Recipe Indexes 2, 3, 5.

Biscuits
  rye, 6
  and soybean, 171
Blancmange, 7
Bread, oatmeal and rye, 5
Cake, plain, 3
Cookies
  chewy crisps, 7
  molasses drop, 8, 169
Crackers, rye, 6
Custard, orange, 171
Floating island, rice, 10
Gingerbread, 3
Muffins, rice and barley, 3
Parfait, pink 'n pretty, 10

Peppers, green, stuffed with hominy,
    171
Pie crust, corn flake or rice flake, 6
Pudding, rice, U.S.A., 10
Rice
  pineapple, 10
  spicy, 10
Sauce
  almond, 7
  cheese, 7
  for creamed dishes, 7
  marmalade, 10
  for scalloped dishes, 7
  white, medium, 7
Shortbread, oat, 3
Veal porkolt or paprika, 5

Index 7: Gluten-, Milk-, and Wheat-Free Recipes

Books indexed are: 3, 8, 169.* *See also* Allergy Recipe Index 2.

Beets, pickled, Palisades, 169*
Bread
  caraway sponge, 8, 169
  corn, 3
Brownies, fudge, 3, 8
Cake *see also* Torte
  banana bread, 3
  chiffon, 3
    orange, 8, 169
  coffee, 3
  jelly roll, Swiss, 3
  lemon, 3
  maple, 3
  peppermint, 3
  sponge
    lemon, 3

Cake, sponge (cont.)
    potato, 8, 169
    upside down
      apricot, 3
      cherry, 169*
Casserole, cod, 169
Cookies
  chocolate chip, 3
  coconut macaroons, 3
  forgotten, 8, 169
  ice box, 3
  orange sponge, 3
  peanut butter, 3, 8, 169
  puff, 3
  sugar, 3
Cream puffs, 3

*In 169, some allergy recipes are not listed in the "Allergy Recipe Index," but in the "Low Calorie Recipe Index"; each such allergy recipe has been identified here by an asterisk (*).

Index 8: Gluten- and Wheat-Free Recipes

Books indexed are: 3, 5, 8, 169. *See also* Allergy Recipe Indexes 2, 3, 7.

Pudding (cont.)
  orange marmalade steamed, 5
  prune, 5
  rice, custard, 169
Sauce
  almond, 3
  caper, 3
  cheese, 3
  for creamed dishes, 3

Sauce (cont.)
  parsley, 3
  for scalloped dishes, 3
  white, 3
Soufflé, cheese, 5
Torte, pumpkin date, 5 *see also* Cake
Waffles, 3, 8
  cornmeal, 169

Index 9: Milk-Free Recipes

Books indexed are: 5, 11. *See also* Allergy Recipe Indexes 2, 4, 5, 7, 10.

Bars, chocolate oatmeal, 11
Bread
  Annette's, 5
  apricot quick, 11
  banana, 5
    orange nut, 5
  date, 5
  pumpkin, 5
Brownies, 5
Cake *see also* Torte
  applesauce, 5
  chiffon, 5
  chocolate, 5
  cranberry orange, 5
  devil's food, 5
  orange, 5
  pumpkin, 5
  raisin, 5

Cake (cont.)
  spice, 5
  upside down, apricot, 5
  white layer, 5, 11
Custard, carrot, 11
Dessert, baked prune whip, 5
Ice cream, Isomil imitation, 11
Meat loaf, 11
Pie
  butterscotch meringue, 11
  custard, baked, 11
  pumpkin, 11
Pudding
  brandy puff, 5
  butterscotch, 11
  prune, Norwegian, 5
Rolls, potato refrigerator, 5
Torte, pumpkin date, 5 *see also* Cake

Index 10: Milk- and Wheat-Free Recipes

Books indexed are: 3, 6, 7, 8, 10, 11, 169, 171. *See also* Allergy Recipe Indexes 2, 5, 7.

Bars *see also* Brownies, Cookies
  chocolate oatmeal, 11
  fig, 6
Blancmange, 11
Bread
  oat, 3
  orange, 3
  prune oatmeal quick, 11
Brownies, rice flour, 10
Cake *see also* Cupcakes
  banana, 3

Cake (cont.)
  chiffon, 6
    giant, 8
  date, 6
  sponge, English, 7
  upside down, apricot, 8
Cookies *see also* Bars, Brownies
  barley, soft, 3, 8
  Chinese chews, 171
  chocolate, 8
  gingerbread men, 8

Cookies (cont.)
 molasses, soft, 8
 molasses snaps, 8
 oat macaroons, 7
 oatmeal, crisp, 8
 oatmeal crunches, 8
 overnight surprises, 8, 169
Cupcakes, chocolate, 8
Custard, baked, 11
Eggnog, fruit flavored, 11
Gingerbread, 8

Muffins, 11
 bacon barley puffs, 171
 corn rye, 8
Pudding
 fig nut, 6
 rice, double boiler, 11
 tapioca, quick, 11
Rice cakes, Calas, 10
Sauce, cherry, 7
Soup, cream of chicken, 11

Index 11: Wheat-Free Recipes

Books indexed are: 2, 3, 5, 6, 7, 8, 9, 10, 171. *See also* Allergy Recipe Indexes 2, 3, 5, 6, 7, 8, 10.

Appetizers
 shrimp balls, 9
 weiners, sweet 'n sour cocktail, 9
Bavarian cream, 9
Bread
 batter, 171
 corn, Southern, 9
 corn rice, 2
 date, 3
 oatmeal nut, 9
 orange frosted, 9
 rice, 2
 rye, 9
 rye potato starch, 2
 rye rice, 2
 soy lima potato, 2
 soy potato, 2
 spoon, 6
Cake *see also* Cupcakes
 banana, 9
 chocolate buttermilk, 8
 coffee, spice crumb, 8
 rice, 2
 rice potato, 2
 soy corn, 2
 soy potato, 2
 soy rice, 2
 sponge, rice flour, 10
Candy
 butterscotch, 2
 fondant, 2

Candy (cont.)
 marshmallows, 2
 panocha, 2
 puffed rice, 2
 soy nut brittle, 2
Casserole, tuna and potato, 9
Cheesecake, 9
Chili casserole, chip 'n, 9
Cookies
 corn crisps, 2
 oatmeal drop, 9, 171
 soy, 2
 soy corn, 2
 soy potato, 2
 soy rice, 2
Corn meal mush, 9
Corn pone, 2
Cupcakes, 7
 soy corn, 2
 soy potato lemon, 2
 soy rice, 2
Custard, caramel, 7
Dessert, apricot pineapple delight, 2
Dressing, meat or poultry, 9 *see also*
  Stuffing
Eggs, with hominy grits, 9, 171
Fish, baked, 10
Frosting and filling
 baked on the cake, 9
 broiled, 2
 caramel, 2

Calorie-Restricted Recipe Index

Books indexed are: 12, 13, 14, 16, 18, 20, 21, 22, 23, 24, 25, 167, 169, 170.

Alaska, baked, orange, 24
Almonds, toasted, 20
Antipasto, 16, 21
Appetizers *see also* Canapés, Dips,
    Spreads
  artichoke ham bites, 14
  carrot sticks, marinated, 169
  citrus cup, spiced, 14
  confetti cocktail, 169
  consommé cubes, jellied, 21
  crudités, 22
  gazpacho cocktail on the rocks, 22
  grapefruit crab cocktail, 14
  holiday cocktail deluxe, 14
  mushroom cocktail, 14
  olives, curried ripe, 169
  pineapple pickups, spiced, 169
  quickies, assorted, 18
  scallops with dip, 14
  shrimp, pickled, 14
  shrimp and apple ball, 169
  Swiss cheese pepper squares, 169
  tomato crab bites, 14
  tomato refresher, hot, 14
  tomato-y cocktail, 23
  tea breaks, variations, 22
  tuna balls, 14
Apple
  Americana, 169
  baked, 16, 20, 21, 22, 23, 170

Apple (cont.)
  with cheese, 24
  surprise, 169
  with sweet cream, 20
  beets, 20
  Bettina, 21
  Betty, marshmallow, 169
  candy jelly, 22
  casserole, marshmallow baked, 18
  compote, 21
  crunch, 12
  delight, 21
  fluff topped berries, 24
  ginger bake, 14
  glazed, 21
  grapefruit combo, 24
  and onions, 170
    medley, 18
  and sauerkraut, 21
  snacks, 170
Applesauce, 21, 23
  instant, 20
  pleasure, 170
Apricot
  apple compote, 170
  brandied, 21
  Melba, 24
  spiced, special, 24
  stewed, 170
Arrolladitos de carne, 18

Diabetic Recipe Index

Books indexed are: 24, 104, 105, 106, 107, 108, 110, 111, 113, 116, 167, 169, 170.

Alaska, baked, 108
Antipasto, caponata, 108
  salad, 108
Appetizers *see also* Canapés, Dips
  carrot sticks, marinated, 169
  celery, sesame-topped stuffed, 169
  cheese nibblers, 113
  clam cocktail, 170
  confetti cocktail (scallops), 169
  crab meat cocktail, 170
  crab meat pie, hot, 169
  cucumber cocktail, grated, 170
  little nibblers (cereal), 105
  shrimp in tomatoes, 107
  vegetables, raw, 167
Apple
  baked, 106, 111, 116, 170
    cinnamon, 108
  Betty, 104, 111
  breakfast, 108
  butter, 105
  crisp, 113, 167
  fluffs, 104
  Kentucky style, 110
Applesauce, 106, 116
Apricot
  purée, 106
  stewed, 106
Artichoke
  bowls, 108
  Italian style, 110
  and mayonnaise, 110

Asparagus
  au gratin, 104
  aux herbes, 169
  and cheese, 106
  Chinese style, 169
  and mushrooms, 107
  par excellence, 111
  spears, seasoned, 169
  on toast, 106
  vinaigrette salad, 169
Aspic 106 *see also* Gelatin, Salad
  beef, soufflé textured, 108
  chicken, soufflé textured, 108
  ham, soufflé textured, 108
  tomato, 104, 167, 169, 170
  tomato with tuna, 104
Bacon, baked, 108
Banana
  baked, 24, 116
  flambées, 110
  frozen, on a stick, 167
  in orange juice, 104, 170
  special, 104, 170
  strawberry fruit cup, 104
Barley, dilled, 169
Bars *see also* Brownies, Cookies
  chocolate, 105
  chocolate angel squares, 105
  fruit, 106
Bauernschmaus, 110
Bavarian cream, 104, 106, 116, 170
  berry-buttermilk, 24

Fat-Controlled Recipe Index

Books indexed are: 59, 60, 61, 62, 63, 64, 65, 66, 67, 69, 70, 71, 80, 81, 167.

Alaska, baked, 67
Almonds
  grilled sugared, 65
  toasted, 65
Antipasto, 61
Appetizers *see also* Canapés, Dips
  artichoke hearts, marinated, 63, 71
  beef chunks, marinated, 64
  beef rolls, dried, 63
  carrot nibblers, 62
  celery sticks, 59
    stuffed, 59, 63, 67
  cereal, snappy, 61
  cereal snacks, 59
  cheese, baked, 59
  cheese corn puffs, 63
  cheese fondue, hot, 70
  cheese puffs, 63
    hoop, 70
  cheese spread, pineapple, 59
  chestnuts, roasted, 63
  chicken spread, easy, 70
  chicken timbales Hawaiian, 71
  chicken walnut pâté, smoked, 63
  Christmas tree relish tray, 61
  clams, steamer, 66
  cottage cheese spread, 59
  crab, curried, in mushrooms, 66
  cranberry relish, 66
  crunchy krisps, 59
  egg whites, stuffed, 67

Appetizers (cont.)
  eggplant, cold, 65
  eggplant salad, 71
  eggs
    stuffed with salmon and capers, 63
    stuffed with tuna and dill, 63
  fish bites with chili dip, 62
  fruit kabobs, 59, 61, 62, 63
  garbanzos, marinated, 61
  garlic rye toasties, 61
  herring, 70
    in sour cream, 66
  kaleidoscope tray, 66
  meat balls, miniature, 61
  meat balls in beer sauce, 61
  melon and dried beef, 63
  mushroom pâté, 63
  mushrooms
    bacon stuffed, 63
    and carrots, pickled, 64
    chilled summer, 63
    elegant hot, 63
    lemon pepper, 61, 63
    marinated, 61, 64, 71
    seasoned, 59
    spiced, 62
  nuts and bolts party mix, 63, 80
  pepper relish, 66
  pickle kabobs, 63
    sweet, 63
  relish, pickled garden, 64

Fat-Restricted Recipe Index

Books indexed are: 57, 84, 85, 86, 168.

Fiber-Restricted Recipe Index

Books indexed are: 55, 56, 57, 168, 169, 170.

Gluten-Restricted Recipe Index

Books indexed are: 5, 145, 146, 147, 149, 150, 151, 167, 171, 173, 176. *See also* Allergy Recipe Indexes 2, 3, 7, 8. (For guidelines on using wheat-free allergy recipes *see* Gluten-restricted Diets, H-1.)

Antojitos, 150
Appetizers
  crêpes
    cheese, bacon, olives, 150
    corned beef and cheese, 150
    dried beef log, 150
    ham and cheese, 150
    peanut and jelly, 150
  puffs, miniature
    blue cheese, 150
    clam, 150
    deviled chicken, 150
    lobster, 150
    sardine, 150
    tuna, 150
Apple
  baked, 146
  cranberry casserole, 149
  meringue, 146
Applesauce
  fluff, 146
  spicy, 146
  whipped, 146
Apricot
  coconut flowers, 149
  pineapple delight, 151
Asparagus Parmesan, 146
Banana
  broiled, 146

Banana (cont.)
  flakes, cottage cheese with, 146
  tropicana, 151
Bars *see also* Brownies, Cookies
  brown sugar chews, 151, 167
  butterscotch, 147, 151
  chocolate squares, p-nutty, 167
  date layer, 145
  date or fig, 145
  fruit, 145
    squares, 151
  Henry's magic, 150
  honey coconut, 149
  jam squares, 173
  peanut butter squares, 151
  squares, variety, 151
Bavarian cream, 146
  apricot, 146
  pineapple, 151
Beans
  green
    Parmesan, 149
    with tagliatelle, 176
  lima, colonial baked, 149
  pinto, barbequed, 149
  refried, 150
  string, in sour cream, 149
Beef
  barbeque rice skillet, 149

Phenylalanine-Restricted Recipe Index

Books indexed are: 154, 155, 156, 164, 171, 173, 174, 175, 176.

Protein-Restricted Recipe Index

Books indexed are: 157, 158, 159, 163, 164, 165, 167, 168, 171, 173, 174 175, 176.

Sodium-Restricted Recipe Index

Books indexed are: 92, 93, 94, 95, 96, 97, 100, 101, 167, 168, 169, 170.

Title Listing of Books Included in Recipe Indexes

Books are listed by entry numbers.

155. *Cookie for a Low-Phenylalanine Diet.* Phenylalanine-restricted.

156. *A Low-Protein, Low-Phenylalanine Vegetable Casserole.* Phenylalanine-restricted.

157. *Practical Low Protein Cookery.* Protein-restricted.

158. *Low Protein Diets for the Treatment of Chronic Renal Failure.* Protein-restricted.

159. *Renal Diet Cookbook.* Protein-restricted.

163. *Gluten-Free Breads for Patients with Uremia.* Protein-restricted.

164. *A Yeast-Leavened, Low-Protein, Low-Electrolyte Bread.* Phenylalanine-restricted; Protein-restricted.

165. *Cal-Power® High Calorie Beverage.* Protein-restricted.

167. *Enjoying Your Restricted Diet.* Calorie-restricted; Diabetic; Fat-controlled; Gluten-restricted; Protein-restricted; Sodium-restricted.

168. *Cooking for Special Diets.* Fat-restricted; Fiber-restricted; Protein-restricted; Sodium-restricted.

169. *Good Housekeeping Cookbook for Calorie Watchers.* Allergy; Calorie-restricted; Diabetic; Fiber-restricted; Sodium-restricted.

170. *The Special Diet Cook Book.* Calorie-restricted; Diabetic; Fiber-restricted; Sodium-restricted.

171. *Food, Nutrition and Diet Therapy.* Allergy; Gluten-restricted; Phenylalanine-restricted; Protein-restricted.

173. *Dietetic Paygel® Baking Mix.* Gluten-restricted; Phenylalanine-restricted; Protein-restricted.

174. *Dietetic Paygel-P® Wheat Starch Recipes.* Phenylalanine-restricted; Protein-restricted.

175. *More Good Things Made with Dietetic Paygel-P™ Wheat Starch.* Phenylalanine-restricted; Protein-restricted.

176. *Recipes for Aproten® Low Protein Imitation Pasta and Porridge.* Gluten-restricted; Phenylalanine-restricted; Protein-restricted.

Bibliography

American Diabetes Assn., Inc. *Cookbook List for Diabetics.* New York, 1973.

American Dietetic Assn. *A Selected Bibliography on the Sodium-Restricted Diet.* Chicago, undated.

American Journal of Clinical Nutrition. Bethesda, Md.

Annals of Allergy. Minneapolis.

Archives of Internal Medicine. Chicago.

Archives of Otolaryngology. Chicago.

Arizona Dietetic Assn. *Nutrition Books for Lay Readers: Recommended; Recommended for Special Purposes; Not Recommended.* Tucson, 1972.

Canadian Dietetic Association Journal. Toronto, Canada.

Chicago Dietetic Supply, Inc. *Information on Allergy Recipes.* Chicago, undated.

Chicago Nutrition Assn. *Nutrition References and Book Reviews.* Chicago, 1972.

Connecticut Dietetic Assn. *References Suitable for Recommendation to Non-Professionals.* New Haven, undated.

Diabetes Education Center. *Bibliography: Cookbooks.* Minneapolis, 1973.

General Mills. *General Nutrition References.* Minneapolis, 1971.
———. *General References for Children and Youth Nutrition.* Minneapolis, 1971.
———. *References and Cookbooks for Diabetic Diets.* Minneapolis, 1971.
———. *References and Cookbooks for Fat Controlled Diets.* Minneapolis, 1971.
———. *References and Cookbooks for Sodium Controlled Diets.* Minneapolis, 1971.
———. *References and Cookbooks for Those on a Bland and/or Fiber Controlled Diet.* Minneapolis, 1971.
———. *References and Cookbooks for Those with Allergies.* Minneapolis, 1971.
———. *References and Cookbooks for Weight Reduction.* Minneapolis, 1971.

Greater Los Angeles Nutrition Council, Inc. *Selected Readings on Foods and Nutrition.* Los Angeles, 1967.

Journal of Nutrition Education. Berkeley, Calif.

Journal of the American Dietetic Association. Chicago.

Journal of the American Medical Association. Chicago.

Kaplan, Doris Flax, R.D., M.L.S. *Selected Bibliography of Nutrition Materials.* Orono, Maine, 1973. University of Maine.

Krause, Marie V., M.S., R.D., Hunscher, Martha A., M.Ed., R.D., M.R.S.H. *Food, Nutrition and Diet Therapy.* Saunders. Philadelphia, 1972.

Los Angeles County Health Dept. *Nutrition Bibliography Series, No. 3, Weight Control.* Los Angeles, 1968.

Los Angeles County Heart Assn. *Bibliography: Recipes and References for Calorie-Controlled, Fat-Controlled and Sodium-Restricted Diets.* Los Angeles, undated.

———*Bibliography of Cardiac Diet Cookbooks.* Los Angeles, undated.

Massachusetts Dept. of Public Health. *Selected Nutrition References.* Boston, 1972.

Missouri Dietetic Assn. *Nutrition Books: Recommended, Recommended for Special Purpose, and Not Recommended.* 1970.

National Dairy Council. *Nutrition News.* Chicago.

National Nutrition Education Clearing House. *Nutrition Information Sources for the Whole Family.* Berkeley, Calif., 1972.

———. *Weight Control—Obesity.* Berkeley, Calif., 1973.

New Jersey Nutrition Council. *Annotated Nutrition Book List.* New Brunswick, 1972, 1973.

New York City Dept. of Health. *Recommended Nutrition Books for Popular Reading.* New York, 1971, 1972.

Nutrition Foundation. *Publications Which Will Assist in Following Medically Prescribed Diet Adjustments.* New York, undated.

———. *Revised Recommended Bibliography.* undated.

———. *Sources of Additional Nutrition Information.* undated.

———. *Nutrition Reviews.* Boston.

Parant, Deborah, R.D. *Sources of Recipes and Menu Suggestions for Diabetics.* New Haven, Conn., undated.

San Francisco Heart Assn. *Suggested List of Recipe Books.* San Francisco, 1973.

Santa Clara–San Mateo Interagency Nutrition Council. *Special Purpose Diet Books.* Stanford, Calif., 1973.

Stare, Fredrick J., M.D.; Witschi, Jelia C., M.S. *Abbreviated List of Nutrition References.* Boston, 1973 (unpublished; prepared for private distribution).

Turner, Dorothea. *Handbook of Diet Therapy.* University of Chicago Press. Chicago, 1965.

University of California Agricultural Extension Service. *Calorie Control.* Berkeley, Calif., 1969.

Ventura County Health Dept. *Special Diet Education Classes Reading List.* Ventura, Calif., 1973.

Ventura County Nutrition Council. *Selected Readings on Food and Health.* Ventura, Calif., 1973.

Washington State Dept. of Health. *Nutrition Bibliography for Public Health Personnel.* Olympia, Wash., 1967, 1972.

———. *Selected Food and Nutrition Books.* Olympia, Wash., 1969, 1973.

Washington State Heart Assn. *Books for Modified Carbohydrate Diets.* Seattle, 1973.

———. *Cookbooks for the Fat Modified Diet.* Seattle, 1972, 1973.

———. *Cookbooks for the Low Sodium Diet.* Seattle, 1973.

APPENDIX I
Directory of Publishers

Alameda County Heart Assn.
4171 MacArthur Blvd.
Oakland, Calif. 94619
  Books: 77, 83, 98, 102

American Diabetes Assn.
1 W. 48 St.
New York, N.Y. 10020
  Books: 104, 118, 119, 144

American Dietetic Assn.
620 N. Michigan Ave.
Chicago, Ill. 60611
  Books: 3, 37, 87, 88, 89, 90, 91, 118,
  126, 127, 155, 156, 163, 164, 209,
  210, 211

American Heart Assn.
44 E. 23 St.
New York, N.Y. 10010
  Books: 75, 76, 78, 79

American Heritage Publishing Co.
1221 Ave. of the Americas
New York, N.Y. 10020
  Books: 35

American Medical Assn.
535 N. Dearborn St.
Chicago, Ill. 60610
  Books: 48, 184, 194, 195

Arco Publishing Co.
219 Park Ave. S.
New York, N.Y. 10003
  Books: 84

Avon Books
The Hearst Corp.
Hearst Magazine Div.
959 Eighth Ave.
New York, N.Y. 10019
  Books: 18

Award Books
Universal Award House, Inc.
235 E. 45 St.
New York, N.Y. 10017
  Books: 21

Ballantine Books, Inc.
201 E. 50 St.
New York, N.Y. 10022
  Books: 199, 205

Bantam Books, Inc.
666 Fifth Ave.
New York, N.Y. 10019
  Books: 14, 20, 72, 92, 182

A. S. Barnes & Co., Inc.
Forsgate Dr.
Cranbury, N.J. 08512
  Books: 4, 5

Berkley Publishing Corp.
200 Madison Ave.
New York, N.Y. 10016
  Books: 54, 67

Best Foods
International Plaza
Englewood Cliffs, N.J. 07632
Books: 7

Campbell Soup Co.
Home Economics Dept.
Campbell Place
Camden, N.J. 08101
Books: 100, 134

Carolyn Busbee Carpenter
237 Pinewood Lane
Rock Hill, S.C. 29730
Books: 149

Chronicle Books
54 Mint St.
San Francisco, Calif. 94103
Books: 66

Cleveland Clinic
9500 Euclid Ave.
Cleveland, Ohio 44106
Books: 85

Thomas Y. Crowell
666 Fifth Ave.
New York, N.Y. 10019
Books: 1

F. A. Davis Co.
1915 Arch St.
Philadelphia, Pa. 19103
Books: 29

Dell Publishing Co., Inc.
245 E. 47 St.
New York, N.Y. 10017
Books: 33

Diabetes Center
1002 E. South Temple
Salt Lake City, Utah 84102
Books: 121

Diabetes Education Center
4959 Excelsior Blvd.
Minneapolis, Minn. 55416
Books: 128, 129, 130

Diabetes Research Fund, Inc.
10208 Wildwood Rd.
Bloomington, Minn. 55437
Books: 105

The Dial Press
245 E. 47 St.
New York, N.Y. 10017
Books: 146

Dietary Research
16035 N.E. Second St.
Bellevue, Wash. 98008
Books: 93

Doubleday & Co., Inc.
Garden City, N.Y., 11530
Books: 59, 92

E. P. Dutton & Co., Inc.
201 Park Ave. S.
New York, N.Y. 10003
Books: 32

Paul S. Eriksson, Inc.
119 W. 57 St.
New York, N.Y. 10019
Books: 16

M. Evans & Co., Inc.
216 E. 49 St.
New York, N.Y. 10017
Books: 34, 55

Farrar, Straus & Giroux, Inc.
19 Union Sq. W.
New York, N.Y. 10003
Books: 68

Fawcett Publications
Fawcett Bldg.
Greenwich, Conn. 06830
Books: 17

Fleischmann's
Nutrition Dept.
P.O. Box 201, Madison Square Station
New York, N.Y. 10010
Books: 81, 94

Frederick Fell Publishers, Inc.
386 Park Ave. S.
New York, N.Y. 10016
  Books: 181

Funk & Wagnalls Publishing Co., Inc.
666 Fifth Ave.
New York, N.Y. 10019
  Books: 19

General Mills Chemicals, Inc.
4620 W. 77 St.
Minneapolis, Minn. 55435
  Books: 165, 173, 174, 175, 176

Ginn & Co.
191 Spring St.
Lexington, Mass. 02173
  Books: 186

Golden Press
1220 Mound Ave.
Racine, Wis. 53404
  Books: 25, 185

Grosset & Dunlap, Inc.
51 Madison Ave.
New York, N.Y. 10010
  Books: 20, 69

Harper & Row, Publishers
10 E. 53 St.
New York, N.Y. 10022
  Books: 63, 107

Hawthorn Books, Inc.
260 Madison Ave.
New York, N.Y. 10016
  Books: 110, 170

Hearst Books
250 W. 55 St.
New York, N.Y. 10019
  Books: 8, 49, 57, 86, 95, 120, 169

Hearthside Press
445 Northern Blvd.
Great Neck, N.Y. 11021
  Books: 22

Holmes Book Co.
274 14 St.
Oakland, Calif. 94607
  Books: 2

The Hospital for Sick Children
555 University Ave.
Toronto, Ontario, Canada
  Books: 151, 152, 153

Intercontinental Medical Book Corp.
381 Park Ave. S.
New York, N.Y. 10016
  Books: 116

Iowa State University Press
Ames, Iowa 50010
  Books: 172, 183

Kansas Wheat Commission
1021 North Main
Hutchinson, Kans. 67501
  Books: 45

Lea & Febiger
600 Washington Sq.
Philadelphia, Pa. 19106
  Books: 2

Eli Lilly & Co.
P.O. Box 618
Indianapolis, Ind. 46206
  Books: 123, 124, 137

J. B. Lippincott Co.
East Washington Sq.
Philadelphia, Pa. 19105
  Books: 73, 115, 177

Little, Brown and Co.
34 Beacon St.
Boston, Mass. 02106
  Books: 60

Los Angeles County Heart Assn.
2405 W. Eighth St.
Los Angeles, Calif. 90057
  Books: 82, 99

Los Angeles District, Calif. Dietetic
    Assn.
Suite 101
1609 Westwood Blvd.
Los Angeles, Calif. 90024
    Books: 136, 160, 161, 166 190

Lutheran General Hospital
1775 Dempster St.
Park Ridge, Ill. 60068
    Books: 125

McCall Publishing Co.
230 Park Ave.
New York, N.Y. 10017
    Books: 15

McGraw-Hill, Inc.
1221 Ave. of the Americas
New York, N.Y. 10020
    Books: 84

David McKay Co., Inc.
750 Third Ave.
New York, N.Y. 10017
    Books: 18, 61

Macmillan, Inc.
866 Third Ave.
New York, N.Y. 10022
    Books: 26

Maryland Dietetic Assn.
1301 York Rd.
Lutherville, Md. 21093
    Books: 159, 162, 180

The Medical Arts Publishing
    Foundation
Distributed by University of Texas Press
Box 7819, University Station
Austin, Tex. 78712
    Books: 106

Medical University Hospital
Dietary Dept.
80 Barre St.
Charleston, S.C. 29401
    Books: 112

Meredith Corp.
1716 Locust St.
Des Moines, Iowa 50336
    Books: 12, 14, 24, 182

Metropolitan Utilities District
1723 Harney St.
Omaha, Nebr. 68102
    Books: 9

National Dairy Council
111 N. Canal St.
Chicago, Ill. 60606
    Books: 38, 39, 40, 41, 187, 188, 189

New York Community Service Society
105 E. 22 St.
New York, N.Y. 10010
    Books: 138

North Dakota Heart Assn.
P.O. Box 1287
Jamestown, N. Dak. 58401
    Books: 80

North Suburban Dietetic Assn. of
    Illinois
1118 Arbor Lane
Glenview, Ill. 60025
    Books: 131

W. W. Norton & Co., Inc.
500 Fifth Ave.
New York, N.Y. 10036
    Books: 56

The Nutrition Foundation, Inc.
99 Park Ave.
New York, N.Y. 10016
    Books: 50, 196, 197, 198

101 Productions
834 Mission St.
San Francisco, Calif. 94103
    Books: 108

Pacific Coast Publishers
4085 Campbell Ave.
Menlo Park, Calif. 94025
    Books: 62

Pacific Press Publishing Assn.
1350 Villa St.
Mountain View, Calif. 94042
   Books: 200, 201, 202, 203, 204, 207

Penguin Books, Inc.
7110 Ambassador Rd.
Baltimore, Md. 21207
   Books: 168

Pillsbury Publications
608 Second Ave. S.
Minneapolis, Minn. 55402
   Books: 23

Pocket Books
630 Fifth Ave.
New York, N.Y. 10020
   Books: 36

Clarkson N. Potter, Inc.
419 Park Ave. S.
New York, N.Y. 10016
   Books: 65

Prentice-Hall, Inc.
Englewood Cliffs, N.J. 07632
   Books: 21, 27, 28

Public Affairs Committee
381 Park Ave. S.
New York, N.Y. 10016
   Books: 51

Pyramid Communications, Inc.
919 Third Ave.
New York, N.Y. 10022
   Books: 1, 74

Henry Regnery Co.
114 W. Illinois St.
Chicago, Ill. 60610
   Books: 64, 71

Research Press
2612 N. Mattis Ave.
Champaign, Ill. 61820
   Books: 30, 31

Rice Council of America
P.O. Box 22802
Houston, Tex. 77027
   Books: 10, 52

Ross Laboratories
625 Cleveland Ave.
Columbus, Ohio 43216
   Books: 11

San Diego County Heart Assn.
3640 Fifth Ave.
San Diego, Calif. 92103
   Books: 70

San Francisco Heart Assn.
259 Geary St.
San Francisco, Calif. 94102
   Books: 96, 97

W. B. Saunders Co.
W. Washington Sq.
Philadelphia, Pa. 19105
   Books: 171

Shadyside Hospital
5230 Centre Ave.
Pittsburgh, Pa. 15232
   Books: 111

Simon & Schuster, Inc.
630 Fifth Ave.
New York, N.Y. 10020
   Books: 13

Southern Publishing Assn.
Box 59
Nashville, Tenn. 37202
   Books: 206

Sunkist Growers
Box 2706
Terminal Annex
Los Angeles, Calif. 90054
   Books: 44

Taplinger Publishing Co., Inc.
200 Park Ave. S.
New York, N.Y. 10003
   Books: 109

Charles C. Thomas
301-27 E. Lawrence Ave.
Springfield, Ill. 62717
   Books: 58, 113, 114, 145, 150, 154, 157, 167

21st Century Communications, Inc.
635 Madison Ave.
New York, N.Y. 10022
  Books: 53

United Fresh Fruit & Vegetable Assn.
777 14th St., N.W.
Washington, D.C. 20005
  Books: 46

U.S. Dept. of Agriculture
See U.S. Government Printing Office

U.S. Dept. of Health, Education and
  Welfare
See U.S. Government Printing Office

U.S. Government Printing Office
Superintendent of Documents
Washington, D.C. 20402
  Books: 6, 42, 43, 178, 179, 191, 192,
  193

U.S. Vitamin Pharmaceutical Corp.
Tuckahoe, N.Y. 10707
  Books: 132, 133, 139, 140, 141, 142,
  143

University Cities Diabetes Education
  Program
733 Taylor Ave.
Moscow, Idaho 83843
  Books: 122

University of Iowa Hospitals
College of Medicine
Iowa City, Iowa 52204
  Books: 117

University of Michigan Medical Center
c/o Dr. Arthur B. French
Clinical Research Unit
Ann Arbor, Mich. 48104
  Books: 147, 148

University of Toronto
c/o Dr. Barbara A. McLaren
Medical Sciences Bldg.
University of Toronto
Toronto 5, Canada
  Books: 101, 103

University of Utah Press
Bldg. 513
Salt Lake City, Utah 84112
  Books: 158

Voice of Prophecy
1500 E. Chevy Chase Dr.
Glendale, Calif. 91206
  Books: 208

David White Co.
60 E. 55 St.
New York, N.Y. 10022
  Books: 72

Worthington Foods, Inc.
Worthington, Ohio 43085
  Books: 47, 135

APPENDIX 2
Retail Mail-Order Suppliers for Special Dietary Foods

The following companies offer retail mail-order service by selling special dietary foods directly to the consumer. Each one publishes a catalog or product list, and will furnish it upon request. Many also offer free recipes to customers, as well as nutritional analyses of their products. Companies that sell exclusively to wholesalers, institutional markets, or to retail stores have not been included.

A summary of the types of diet-related products offered is given for each retailer. Some carry a wide range of foods, and may offer a dozen or more types of ingredient control. Others tend to specialize in a few kinds of food and types of ingredient control. Readers interested in only one or two types of ingredient control will be assisted by the chart (Fig. 2) which shows the type of ingredient control in dietary foods that each retail mail-order supplier usually handles. This information should not be interpreted to mean that a supplier offers all types of ingredient control shown for every product available. Normally, only one or two types of ingredient control are important.

Serial letters to identify retailers are employed not only in the Ingredient Control Chart but also in Appendix 3: Brand Name Availability List, which permits the reader to locate suppliers for specific brand name products.

A. Adolph's Ltd., P.O. Box 828, Burbank, Calif. 91503
    condiments; flour; salt substitutes; sweetener, artificial

B. Bernard Food Industries, Inc.; 222 S. 24 St., San Jose, Calif. 95103
    baking mix; cake/mixes; condiments; flavoring; flour; gelatin/mixes; icing; jam/jelly; pudding/mixes; salad dressing; soup; sweetener, artificial

C. Byrd Mill Co., P.O. Box 5167, Richmond, Va. 23220
    flour

D. Chicago Dietetic Supply, Inc., 405 E. Shawmut Ave., La Grange, Ill. 60525
    baking mix; baking powder; beverages; bread/mixes; cake/mixes; candy; cereal; cheese; condiments; cookies/mixes; egg substitutes; flour; fruits; gelatin/mixes; jam/jelly; juice; meats/poultry; pasta/macaroni/spaghetti; peanut butter; pickles; pie filling; pudding/mixes; salad dressing; salt substitutes; seafood; soup; sweetener, artificial; syrup; vegetables

284

E. Diamond Crystal Salt Co., 10 Burlington Ave., Wilmington, Mass. 01887

salt substitutes; sweetener, artificial

F. Ener-G Foods, Inc., 1526 Utah Ave. S., Seattle, Wash. 98134

bread/mixes

G. Estee Candy Co., Inc., 169 Lackawanna Ave., Parsippany, N.J. 07054

candy; chewing gum

H. Fisher Cheese Co., P.O. Box 409, Wapakoneta, Ohio 45895

cheese

I. General Mills, Inc., 4620 W. 77 St., Dept. 175, Minneapolis, Minn. 55435

baking mix; beverages; bread/mixes; cereal; egg substitutes; flour; pasta/macaroni/spaghetti

J. Hudson Pharmaceutical Corp., 21 Henderson Dr., Caldwell, N.J. 07006

salt substitute; sweetener, artificial

K. J. R. Kennedy Co., 1441 W. 46 Ave., Unit #1, Denver, Colo. 80211

flavoring

L. Kingsmill Food Co., Ltd., 280 Nantucket Blvd., Scarborough, Ontario, Canada

flour

M. MacDowell Brothers, P.O. Box 141, Ogdensburg, N.Y. 13669

baking powder; cookies/mixes; flour; sweetener, artificial

N. T. Marzetti Co., P.O. Box 29163, Columbus, Ohio 43229

salad dressing

O. Sta-Wel Nutrition Centers, Inc., 16 W. 40 St., New York, N.Y. 10018

baking powder; beverages; bread/mixes; cake/mixes; candy; cereal; cheese; condiments; cookies/mixes; flour; fruits; gelatin/mixes; jam/jelly; juice; margarine / butter; meats/poultry; milk substitutes; pasta/macaroni/spaghetti; peanut butter; pickles; pie filling; pudding/mixes; salad dressing; salt substitutes; seafood; soup; sweetener, artificial; syrup; textured vegetable protein; vegetables

P. Sugarless Candy Corp. of America, 3537 W. North Ave., Chicago, Ill. 60647

cake/mixes; candy

Q. U.S. Health Club, Inc., P.O. Box 293, Yonkers, N.Y. 10701

candy; flour

Ingredient Control	A	B	C	D	E	F	G	H	I	J	K	L	M	N	O	P	Q
calorie-restricted	√	√		√	√		√	√		√	√		√	√	√	√	
cereal-free		√		√											√		
chocolate-free				√			√								√	√	√
corn-free			√	√									√		√		√
egg-free				√											√		
fat-controlled	√	√		√				√	√					√	√		
fat-restricted	√	√		√				√			√			√	√		
gluten-restricted			√	√		√			√			√	√		√		√
high caloric									√								
milk-free				√		√									√		
phenylalanine-restricted				√		√			√						√		
protein-restricted			√	√		√			√			√	√		√		
sodium-restricted	√	√		√	√	√			√	√		√	√		√	√	
wheat-free				√		√						√	√				√

Figure 2. *Retail Mail-Order Suppliers.*

APPENDIX 3
Brand Name Availability List

The following brand names are available from retailers indicated here by serial letter. (For the full name and address of the supplier see Appendix 2, Retail Mail Order Suppliers.)

Adolph's: **A, O**

Amurol: **O**

Aproten: **D, I**

Arcadia: **O**

Bac-N-Salt: **K**

Balanced: **O**

Battle Creek: **O**

Bernard: **B**

But-R-Salt: **K**

Byrd Mill: **C**

Cal-Power: **I**

Campbells: **O**

Cellu: **D, O**

Ceres: **O**

Cheez-ola: **H**

Chico-San: **O**

Chono: **I**

Count Down: **H**

D-Zerta: **O**

De Boles: **O**

Devonshire: **O**

Diamel: **O**

Diamond Butter: **O**

Diamond Crystal: **E**

Diasal: **O**

Diet-Jell: **O**

Dietician: **O**

Drakes: **O**

Droste: **O**

Dwarf: **O**

El Molino: **O**

Elam's: **O**

Ener-G: **F**

Energen: **O**

Estee: **G, O**

Fanfare: **O**

Farley's: **M, O**

Fearn: **O, Q**

Featherweight: **D, O**

Fisher: **H**

Fortissimo: **O**

Frenchette: **N**

General Mills: **I**

Greyslake: **O**

Grielle: **O**

Hain: **O**

Health-Wise: **Q**

Hol Grain: **O**

House of Herbs: **O**

Hudson: **J**

Joan's: **G**

Jolly Joan: **F, O**

Jireh: **M**

Kennedy, J. R.: **K**

Lihn: **O**

Lister's: **M**

Lo Pro: **D**

Loma Linda: **O**

London House: **B**

MacDowell's: **M**

Madison: **O**

Marra: **O**

Marzetti: **N**

Master: **D, O**

Mayonette Gold: **N**

Meeters: **O**

Milani: **O**

Mother's: **O**

Nu-Salt: **O**

Nu-Vita: **O**

Paygel: **I**

Pfaffman's: **O**

Polander: **O**

Pro-Teen: **O**

Plantation: **O**

Reese: **O**

San Martin: **O**

Sherman's: **O**

Smithers: **O**

Sokeland's: **O**

Soy-O: **Q**

Soyagen: **O**

Soyalac: **O**

Soyamel: **O**

Spice o' Life: **B**

Sta-Wel: **O**

Sucaryl: **O**

Sug'r Like: **D**

Sugarless: **P**

Sunnydale Academy: **O**

Supreme: **O**

Sweet Jane: **O**

Tartex: **O**

3V: **O**

Town: **O**

Unimix: **L**

Van Brode: **O**

Veta-Roni: **O**

Vogue: **O**

Waferets: **O**

Waylow: **D**

Wilderness: **O**

Worthington: **O**

Wuest: **O**

Ye Old Farm: **O**

Author Index

Listings below refer to entry numbers.

Title Index

Listings below refer to entry numbers.

Subject Index

Listings below refer to entry numbers.